FALKIRK DISTRICT COUNCIL

30124 01331710 4

C000007742

CANCELLED

22. 06. 96

Quality Assurance

A Framework To Build On

Quality Assurance

A Framework To Build On

Terry Hughes FRICS

Trefor Williams BSc

Copyright © Terry Hughes & Trefor Williams
1991

BSP Professional Books
A division of Blackwell Scientific
  Publications Ltd
Editorial offices:
Osney Mead, Oxford OX2 0EL
25 John Street, London WC1N 2BL
23 Ainslie Place, Edinburgh EH3 6AJ
3 Cambridge Center, Cambridge
  MA 021412, USA
54 University Street, Carlton,
  Victoria 3053, Australia

All rights reserved. No part of this
publication may be reproduced, stored
in a retrieval system, or transmitted
in any form or by any means, electronic,
mechanical, photocopying, recording
or otherwise without the prior
permission of the copyright owner.

First published 1991

Printed and bound in Great Britain
by the University Press, Cambridge

FALKIRK DISTRICT LIBRARIES

658·562   FK

DISTRIBUTORS

Marston Book Services Ltd
PO Box 87
Oxford OX2 0DT
(*Orders:*   Tel: 0865 791155
             Fax: 0865 791927
             Telex: 837515)

USA
  Blackwell Scientific Publications, Inc.
  3 Cambridge Center
  Cambridge, MA 02142
  (*Orders:* Tel: (800) 759-6102)

Canada
  Oxford University Press
  70 Wynford Drive
  Don Mills
  Ontario M3C 1J9
  (*Orders:* Tel: (416) 441-2941)

Australia
  Blackwell Scientific Publications
  (Australia) Pty Ltd
  54 University Street
  Carlton, Victoria 3053
  (*Orders:* Tel: (03) 347-0300)

British Library
Cataloguing in Publication Data
Hughes, T.B.
    Quality assurance: a framework to build on.
    1. Civil engineering. Quality control
    I. Title II. Williams, T.
    624.0685

ISBN 0-632-02849-1

CONTENTS

PREFACE

1 INTRODUCTION   1

    1.0   Background   1

    1.1   The three factors that management must consider   1

    1.2   Quality assurance   3

    1.3   What a QA system is trying to do   8

2 SYNOPSIS OF BS 5750 : PART 2 : 1987.   11

    2.0   General   11

    2.1   Philosophy of BS 5750   11

    2.2   Synopsis of BS 5750 : Part 2 clauses   12

        2.2.1   Management (Clause 4.1)   14

        2.2.2   QA system (Clause 4.2)   15

        2.2.3   Contract review (Clause 4.3)   16

        2.2.4   Document control (Clause 4.4)   17

        2.2.5   Purchasing (Clause 4.5)   18

        2.2.6   Process control (Clause 4.8)   19

        2.2.7   Inspection and testing (Clause 4.9)   20

        2.2.8   Handling and storage (Clause 4.14)   21

        2.2.9   Quality records (Clause 4.15)   22

        2.2.10 Audit (Clause 4.16)   23

        2.2.11 Training (Clause 4.17)   24

3 IMPLEMENTATION   25

    3.0   Generally   25

    3.1   Instigation   27

    3.2   Investigation   27

    3.3   Development   35

    3.4   Testing   35

4 THE SYSTEM DEVELOPED - ITS STRUCTURE AND PHILOSOPHY   39

    4.0   Structure of the system developed   39

    4.1   Philosophy of the system developed   42

    4.2   The system developed   44

    4.3   The operation of the system   47

5 THE SYSTEM DEVELOPED - TENDER STAGE   49

    5.0   The points addressed   49

    5.1   Issues considered under the relevant BS headings   49

    QA Manual extract   54

6 THE SYSTEM DEVELOPED - MOBILISATION STAGE   77

    6.0   The points addressed   77

    6.1   Issues considered under the relevant BS headings   78

    QA Manual extract   80

7 THE SYSTEM DEVELOPED - CONSTRUCTION STAGE   83

    7.0   The points addressed   83

    7.1   Issues considered under the relevant BS headings   84

    QA Manual extract   86

8 THE SYSTEM DEVELOPED - GENERAL PROCEDURES   97

    8.0   Introduction   97

    8.1   Document Control Procedures   97

    8.2   Quality Plan Procedures   97

    QA Manual extract   99

9 THE SYSTEM DEVELOPED - OTHER ISSUES   121

    9.0   General   121

    9.1   Audit, records and feedback   121

    9.2   The Quality Manager   123

    9.3   Recruitment, Education and Training   124

    9.4   Familiarisation   125

10 FORMS   127

    10.0   Introduction   127

11 CONCLUSION   167

    11.0   Generally   167

    11.1   Summary of 20 key points   167

INDEX   171

Quality Assurance (QA) is a subject which attracts either firm supporters or vociferous detractors. Those that are critical point to the impracticality of applying such a philosophy to their own organisations. The criticisms however are often made on the basis of indifferent knowledge or experience.

This book is written for people involved in construction management who have heard of QA and wish to look in some depth at what the implementation of such a philosophy would mean. The book describes the methods used in producing a particular system and details the principle elements involved.

The book has used as its basis not the theory that has already been widely covered but a practical example. This example is drawn from twelve months' work within a contractor's organisation developing a workable Quality Assurance Management System. The system has been developed with the problems of a particular company in mind as well as providing the necessary attributes required by the British Standard. However, the majority of problems discovered are common within the industry and will probably be recognised by most readers.

All flow charts, forms and procedures used in this book have been edited from their original form but still contain all the basic ingredients necessary for an integrated QA system.

Quality in this context means achieving the 'specified requirements' or getting it right. QA has the aim of getting things right first time. This aim is to be achieved first by documenting what you do and how you do it, second by checking that it is done, and finally by recording that fact. This process of writing down what you do, together with the checking and recording procedures, provides the client with the assurance that you are aiming to get it right.

It is obvious to anyone in the business of construction that this aim is presently difficult to achieve with consistency. Managers recognise that controlling what they do and how they do it, has become more difficult. They also recognise that where control is limited, profitability becomes an erratic commodity.

QA aims to provide a platform on which consistent improvement can be developed. The difference between successful and unsuccessful projects is often no more than doing a number of small things at the right time and in the right way. The problem is identifying them in time to ensure that they are done. QA provides the means by which this can be achieved.

If some common sense aspects of management are ignored the introduction of QA can be counterproductive. Accordingly the system must not be inflexible or dictatorial, but should encourage communication.

In terms of construction organisations it is generally recognised that management must build and foster an efficient team. To accomplish this, research recommends a style of management which is highly considerate and also highly structured.

These aims are not contradictory as some would think. It is possible to produce a management system that is both considerate of the individual, allowing innovation, and structured to control the way tasks are undertaken.

A well thought out QA system does not produce a managerial strait jacket, but a coat which touches where it must and provides room for movement whenever it can. It allows business organisations to have checkable procedures without binding everyone with unnecessary constraints.

It will be seen in reading this book that the way that the system was developed takes care, whenever possible, to allow the individual to introduce innovation. At the same time the system provides a structure which management can monitor and control. It is important to consider these aims should you wish to modify sections of the system for your own use.

QA is a subject which the industry cannot ignore. It is already widely used in manufacturing and will spread through client-led demand to most areas of construction.

A QA system involves no great changes for an efficient well organised company. Much of what is required may already be done, it merely needs formalising and recording. You may be further down the road to a QA system than you think.

Before looking at QA systems it is worth noting the principle reasons identified by auditors when analysing unsuccessful systems:

- company's only aim was to obtain a registration badge and not to improve quality
- consultants/management produce a system then impose it upon employees
- poor communication, resulting in employees not understanding how and why the system operated
- quality system operating in parallel with existing management systems rather than being integrated.

The authors hope that with the assistance of this book these pitfalls will be avoided.

The authors would like to acknowledge the help of Jonathan Hall and Terry Powell in the production of this book.

PREFACE

1.0   Background

Within the construction industry it is recognised that an increasing amount of time is being spent in the preparation or examination of contractual claims. It has also become apparent that for a variety of reasons there is a diminishing return from such claims. A key to this is the increased sophistication of clients in applying the requirements of the Standard Forms of Building Contract. These contracts clearly place the burden of proof on the contractor. The task of providing this proof, often in the form of documentary evidence, is frequently complicated by a lack of pertinent records. A failure to promptly provide the required documents disturbs the relationship between contractor and client or more particularly the client's agent. Therefore to make things worse economic loss is often accompanied by loss of goodwill. In addition when tracing the history of some of these disputes it becomes clear that the problems which form the basis of these claims, although frequently materialising at site level, regularly have had their root cause earlier in the management and design process.

Examination of project records shows that questions have not been asked when they should have been, problems are not seen until after they have occurred. It is typically not the case that the individuals involved lack expertise or initiative. It is more often the case that they are pressed for time by other concerns resulting in them giving these issues scant attention. A further difficulty arises where an individual's lack of experience limits their personal horizon and dims their perspective of the problems ahead. Crises caused by poor quality have often overtaken contracts that appeared to be proceeding successfully, with the resulting delay and cost, undoing the supposed benefits that had been accrued.

It is clear that as the cost of getting it wrong increases, regardless of which party is at fault, the cost of getting it right becomes the sensible economic objective.

1.1   The three factors that management must consider

One of the major problems encountered is an over emphasis by management on time and cost. These are important factors but are only two parts of what is in effect a three-sided triangle of time, cost and quality. These factors must be in balance as any neglect of one will have a corresponding detrimental effect upon the other two. This follows the mathematical rule that an alteration to any angle in a triangle will amend one or both of the other angles. Historically there has been an attempt to manage the construction process by controlling time and cost in progress whilst quality tends to be managed in retrospect. This is understandable since most management control systems highlight time and cost and leave the responsibility for quality to others.

It is our contention that quality in the true sense of the word must be given equal priority with time and cost within contractors' management processes.

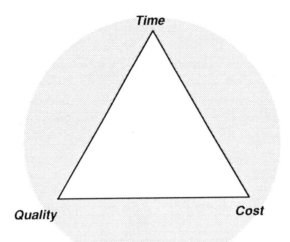

Fig 1.1 The three factors

From this viewpoint of retrieving the balance between concerns for time, cost and quality an interest in quality assurance developed. At first there was no clear indication of how quality systems could overcome the problems. On first examination quality assurance produces scepticism. Why should the introduction of even more forms and procedures, to an industry already overburdened with them, improve the situation. However continuing interest and research led to the opportunity to assist in the development of a Quality Assurance management system for a contractor's organisation.

The result of this work was an understanding and appreciation of how the contents and process of development necessary for a QA system can in large measure be:

- an answer to many of the problems seen
- not at all the generator of paperwork imagined.

As many managers are aware, frequently by the time site management has become involved in the project the problems are already there, at embryo stage, hidden by a mass of paperwork. A means must be produced to find these problems at this embryonic and less costly stage. QA requires you to define in writing precisely what you do. This very task produces a means of identifying where these problems are likely to occur, highlighting the important from the mundane, the unusual from the commonplace.

Put simply:

QA system means	Results in
* Efficient use of time	* Time available to site manager
* Addressing items in good time	
* Providing solutions drawn from past experience of others	* Source of 'experience' for site manager
* Placing responsibility where it is intended to be	* Source of records if required
* Generating pertinent records	* A means of measuring performance

1.2   Quality assurance

1.2.1 Why

Commercial reasons

Contracting has always involved the acceptance of risk. The secret of success has been to keep the risk within confined and controllable limits.

The risks currently associated with the discovery of defective work are increasing in both the long and short term.

Long Term Latent Damage Act 1986 - 15 years liability with the period of liability running from date of discovery.

Short Term The Intermediate Form of Contract introduced with clause 3.13.1. - a new power for architects following the discovery of defects to establish *at no cost to the employer* that no similar failure exists.

This has now been extended to JCT 80 with the introduction of clause 8.4 allowing the architect this same power provided his instructions are *reasonable*. The extent of risk is increasing both in terms of liability, occurrence and cost.

Liability The contractor's share of risk is being expanded from a number of sources:

- legal decisions - duty of care. A tendency toward consumer protection is likely to lead to an expansion of legal liability
- contract amendments - JCT 80 clause 1.4 states that, not withstanding the architect's obligations, the contractor is *fully* responsible. Pressures on architects via their professional indemnity insurance will continue this trend
- client/client's agents' resistance to contractual claims has meant diminishing returns from this process.

Occurrence The frequency of discovery of defective construction has been highlighted in a number of recent reports.

In the shorter term contractors can expect to find increasing pressure for compliance with better draughted specifications particularly from the PSA who are currently in the forefront of design/supervision orientated QA developments. Government support is likely to expand this to other areas of public expenditure.

Cost It is recognised that the cost of rectifying defects increases in relation to progress. The later the problem is found the more expensive it is to put right. Fig 1.2 could show for example the cost profile of remedying a foundation concrete problem.

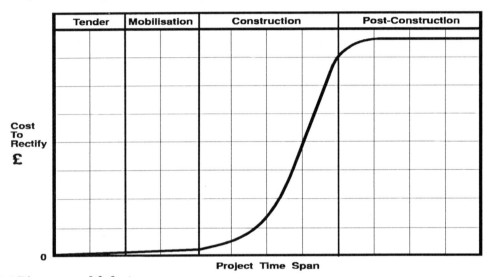

Fig 1.2 Discovery of defect

Marketing reasons

Improved image You can sell on perceived quality, as well as price, Marks & Spencer and Jaguar Cars being prime examples.

Bandwagon Clients are increasingly asking for a company's quality credentials which often equates to inclusion or exclusion from tender lists.

Type of market Ability to tender for work in a more selective market.

Organisational reasons

There is a shortage both in terms of quantity and quality of skilled labour and supervision.

Contractors not only have difficulty in obtaining experienced labour but also in obtaining acceptable standards of work from the labour available.

QUALITY ASSURANCE

Labour today is generally employed on a labour only basis and is largely motivated by income. A problem associated with this is that they recognise that their income can be increased in four principle ways:

- working longer hours
- pushing up rates per unit of output
- cutting corners to increase output
- working for a well organised main contractor.

Companies should aim to ensure that the final choice of working for a well organised contractor is available. For the above reasons the need for experienced competent supervision has never been greater. Supervision skills are currently, and for the foreseeable future going to be, in short supply. When this is combined with the greater administrative burden that legal obligations and tighter schedules impose the problems of control are exacerbated. A further difficulty apparent within contractors' supervisory structures are the disparate skills required for planning, control and motivation, strengths in the practical skills often going hand in hand with poor administrative skills and vice versa.

1.2.2 How

Options to improve quality:

- improve supervision and inspection
- build-in quality using a systems approach.

Improve supervision and inspection

Traditionally quality control has involved inspection and testing as the work proceeds. Although increased supervision and inspection can improve the performance and quality on site there are several disadvantages of this option.

1. Increased cost of supervisory staff.
2. The nature of building sites makes it almost impossible to inspect every stage of the work.
3. This option is not always able to predict difficulties but has to provide solutions as and when they arise. (management by crisis)
4. Testing is retrospective and thus costly to remedy faults.

Furthermore evidence in manufacturing industry has shown that even extremely sophisticated inspection measures in a controlled environment have only a limited and temporary success

Systems approach

An alternative to increased supervision is to adopt quality systems. These systems provide a way of working that either prevents problems arising or identifies and deals with them effectively and cheaply if they arise. The emphasis is on fire prevention rather than fire fighting.

Addressing these problems early enables management to be proactive. Systems identify when tasks are being carried out correctly or whether they have been carried out at all. They allow a manager to manage, but more importantly are a means of directing employees towards what needs to be done.

1.2.3 What

Quality is defined in BS 4778 : Part l : 1987 as *The totality of features and characteristics of a product or service that bear on its ability to satisfy stated and implied needs.*

In the construction industry the technique, known as 'Quality Assurance', had previously only been applied to high value projects where public safety and integrity of construction was of paramount importance, e.g. nuclear installations, offshore structures, etc. Outside these sectors of the industry there had been little or no commercial incentive for professionals and contractors alike involved with the industry to introduce QA. However, since the publication of a Government White Paper in 1982 entitled 'Standards Quality and International Competitiveness', followed by a National Quality Campaign, greater impetus was given to the wider use of the concept and its development into more commercial areas.

Beneath the jargon-ridden mystique the principles of QA are really quite simple. These are to devise methods of doing work systematically so as to avoid errors and costly mistakes.

A QA system has been commonly described as:

- saying what you do
- doing what you say
- recording that you have done it.

Saying what you do

A simple statement which belies the very complex task necessary to achieve it. The statement 'say what you do' can be looked at from different perspectives each of which would consider that statement in differing depths e.g. the managing director's overview is not always the same as the employee's perspective of the task. A good QA system should therefore view this statement from the perspective of those who have to undertake the tasks described.

Doing what you say

Is an action following the written statement of your intentions in the preceding item. It should be appreciated that the greater the detail used to describe what you do, the easier it should be for the individual to follow it. In tandem with this it is important that the detail is a faithful description of how various tasks are executed. If not it will soon become apparent that the system is merely what you wish would happen and not what does happen, thereby devaluing its usefulness.

Recording that you have done it

Having both defined and performed the tasks it is necessary to produce evidence that this has in fact occurred. Such records are useful to the individuals that have carried out the task, their superiors who have the responsibility for ensuring the task is undertaken and to third parties who require the provision of such evidence.

1.2.4 Advantages and disadvantages of systems approach

Advantages derived from available research data are:

1. Improved communications and efficiency.
2. Checking of work and avoidance of unnecessary and costly errors, failures and expensive remedial works.
3. Documented proof that work has been executed in compliance with the document and specifications.
4. Easier implementation of client changes.
5. Precise clarification and quantification of the effects of such changes.
6. Easier identification and quantification of delays and claims.
7. Completion on time.
8. Reduced maintenance period remedial works.
9. Provision of as-built records.
10. Possible reduction of insurance premiums.
11. Improved competitiveness and marketability of services.

Disadvantages

There are three main problems which have been identified

Need to retain records Can be costly and take up space. However it is not certain as yet how much information will need to be stored or for how long. It is possible that individual clients will agree on the extent and duration of document retention.

Additional staff requirements Experience seems to indicate that additional staff are required during establishment and implementation. If there are any additional staff costs they will probably be far outweighed by the eventual long term benefits previously outlined.

Start-up costs and certification charges Precise figures are obviously difficult to obtain but research seems to suggest that full establishment of systems with third party certification would represent about 0.3% of one year's turnover over a period of two years i.e. 0.15% each year.

1.3 What a QA system is trying to do

It is the production of a checkable written guide for the use of individuals. These include employees, managers and third parties.

It produces a template for the individual employee to use in performing their particular tasks, that the manager can use in ensuring the proper performance of those tasks and that the client or third party can use to confirm that their requirements have been met.

Managers benefit as individuals performing their own tasks and are assisted in their leadership function. The definition of subordinates' and colleagues' roles and responsibilities together with lines of communication and evidence of performance provides a clearer means of control.

Third parties, even more than managers, appreciate they cannot check that all tasks have been executed in accordance with their requirements. The system gives them this assurance and overcomes the uncheckable nature of some tasks. An extreme example of how this confidence operates is the American Corps of Engineers who rely for quality solely on the assurance provided by their QA certified contractors. There is however a sting in the tail of this apparent blind faith in that should any contractor be found to have not complied with the requirements of their QA system they may immediately be precluded from any future work.

Individuals that we have interviewed who have used such a system have appreciated its benefits in that the system as a whole describes both the organisation, including their roles, and the tasks they are required to perform. A common statement from them was that the system enabled them on joining the organisation or project to know what their roles were and what was expected of them. They can quickly fit in and feel involved.

1.3.1 Implementation

For any QA system to be meaningful it must include assessment and certification. There are three main grades of QA system each related to the choice of certifying party. Thus you can have first, second or third party certified systems each with varying degrees of acredibility and thus acceptability, although to have any credibility at all systems must comply with BS 5750. This issue is explained in more detail on page 25.

In addition the level of certification sought can vary:

- to include or exclude design i.e. BS 5750 : Part 1 includes design, BS 5750 : Part 2 excludes design
- to set a minimum value e.g. the system will only apply on projects exceeding £1M
- to be applicable to specific project type only e.g. housing.

Certifiers stipulate that a third party system must be applicable to a significant part of the company's operations.

The grade and level of certification chosen may be subsequently extended by expanding the coverage of the original system developed.

The need for a QA system can develop either from a second party's requirements or from the recognition by management of inherent problems within the company's organisation. Whichever is the source it is necessary if the organisation is to develop a factual rather than a fictional system that a belief and commitment to producing quality exists. A QA system is not an 'optional extra' only to be used when required but is a philosophy which must be totally integrated with the company's existing management systems. Unless the top management believe that QA will provide a benefit to their organisation then it is unlikely that the system subsequently developed will actually achieve all that it is intended to. A commitment to QA will invariably mean changing the way things are done at present and require that discipline is imposed on the whole of an organisation from the top down.

Experience and research has indicated that in producing a QA system organisations tend to encounter two major problems:

1. Not appreciating the volume of work required to prepare a system e.g. they will appoint an individual from within the organisation to prepare the QA system, frequently in addition to their other duties. This leads to one of two results:

    *   the task becomes elongated leading to a loss of impetus or

    *   the individual will address the problems in less depth than is actually required, producing an ineffective system.

2. Balancing the need for both a knowledge of QA and an understanding of the functioning of the organisation. This is best illustrated by the continuum shown below:

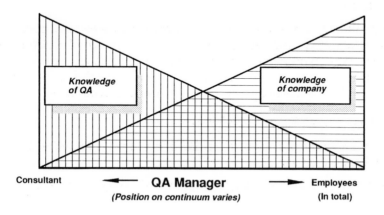

Fig 1.3 Knowledge continuum

The use of QA consultants in most cases tends to span a relatively short proportion of the total period required for the preparation of a system. Also it tends to occur at or near the start of that process. Whilst the QA consultant will provide you with the basic philosophy of a QA system they often lack knowledge of the tasks that such a system must address. This knowledge rests very much with the totality of individuals within the organisation. Managers can give you the overall picture of the tasks that are undertaken. Only the individuals responsible can describe how those tasks are executed in sufficient detail for your analysis. The problem is reconciling knowledge of the company and quality assurance at the right time i.e. the QA consultant's advice is frequently received before a full appreciation of the scale of the problems is available. The appointment of a QA Manager provides an interface between these sources although his own knowledge of either aspect will vary. A more detailed discussion of the role of the QA Manager can be found in Chapter 9.

Our book seeks to provide some remedies to these problems. It will firstly provide a skeleton to substantially reduce the hundreds, possibly thousands, of manhours necessary in establishing relatively common processes and procedures. Secondly it enables the company to look ahead at an early stage when the QA consultant is still closely involved. This knowledge will enable a more effective use to be made of a relatively expensive asset.

The next chapter is a synopsis of BS 5750 : Part 2 : 1987 and relates the terminology used therein to the construction process.

2.0   General

As noted in the previous chapter, a company's QA system should comply with BS 5750. This British Standard is produced in four parts:

Part 1   Specification for design/development, production, installation and servicing.

Part 2   Specification for production and installation.

Part 3   Specification for final inspection and test.

Part 4   Guide to the use of Parts 1 to 3.

BS 5750 : Part 2 : 1987, excludes design and is therefore the appropriate choice for controlling a construction company's traditional activities. A contractor's design and build projects can also be covered under this Part of the British Standard provided the design is bought-in. Otherwise compliance with Part 1 would be necessary which would add to and amend some of the clauses discussed within this chapter.

2.1   Philosophy of BS 5750

The philosophy is that in order for a company to be successful it must offer products or services that:

1.   Meet a well defined need, use or purpose.
2.   Satisfy customers' expectations.
3.   Comply with applicable standards and specifications.
4.   Comply with statutory (and other) requirements of society.
5.   Are made available at competitive prices.
6.   Are provided at a cost which will yield a profit.

The means by which this is achieved is through a system of quality management which aims to 'get it right first time'. Client assurance requires demonstration of an organisation's capability to control the processes that determine the acceptability of the product supplied. The requirements of the Standard are aimed primarily at preventing and detecting any nonconformity during production and installation. This includes the implementation of a means of preventing its recurrence.

It is applicable in contractual situations when:

- the specified requirements for the product are stated in terms of an established design or specification. Two definitions of specified requirements are given within BS 5750: Part 4: 1990
- confidence in product conformance can be attained by adequate demonstration of a certain supplier's capabilities in production and installation.

Whilst the above statement is of course true you will find in practice that it is difficult to merely use these principles on a selective basis only. The process of development of a workable QA system explores many facets of an organisation's existing procedures and structure. Existing company procedures will almost certainly be amended during the development of a QA system and the likelihood of the company devising two new procedures, one to operate with QA and the other without, is remote.

2.2   Synopsis of BS 5750 : Part 2 clauses

Figure 2.1 is a diagramatic representation of the requirements of BS 5750 : Part 2 : 1987 Quality Systems. The shadowed boxes represent the majority of the BS clause numbers, with the balance being shown as links between the various elements e.g. Traceability Clause 4.7. The shadowed boxes are linked to represent the interrelationship of each of the clauses within a quality system. The quality system itself, Clause 4.2, is shown double boxed as it represents the repository of the information shown on the remainder of the diagram. In addition to the shadowed boxes and their links, other boxes are included to represent other elements found within the construction process but not specifically referred to in the British Standard. Although the system operates throughout the company the diagram also indicates that certain elements are primarily project specific.

The synopsis hereafter gives a brief interpretation of each of the clauses within the British Standard and explains how the diagram links these various elements together.

Each of the clauses noted on diagram Fig 2.1 is examined as follows:

- each page starts with a brief interpretation of the essential features of the clause
- below this is an extract from the diagram shown in Fig 2.1. together with a description of that element and its relationship to the other clauses
- finally there may be some additional notes of explanation.

For further information refer to BS 5750 : Part 4 : 1990 and CIRIA Special Publication 74 Interpretations of BS 5750 (1987).

QUALITY ASSURANCE

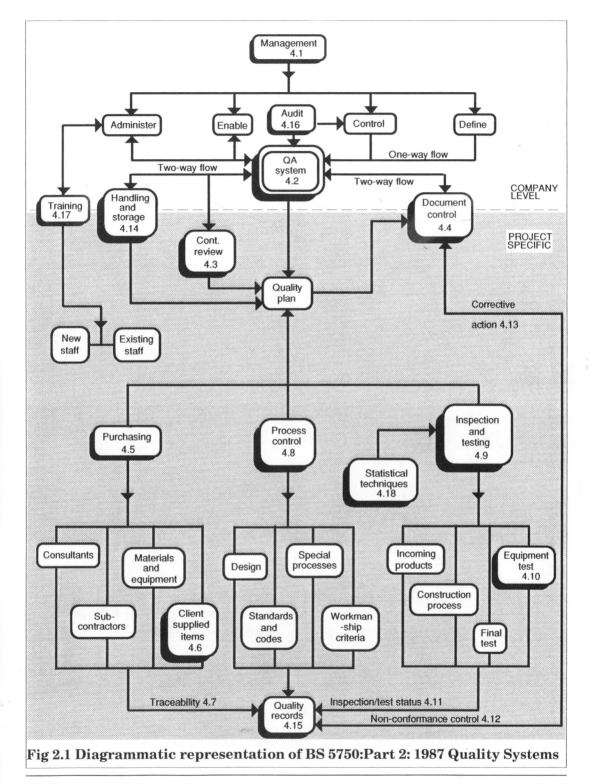

Fig 2.1 Diagrammatic representation of BS 5750:Part 2: 1987 Quality Systems

2.2.1 Management (Clause 4.1)

Management must:

Define

State its policy and objectives which contain the quality intentions and direction of the organisation.

The quality system must be implemented from the top down under the guidance of the Senior Manager.

Enable

Delegate in writing defining the responsibility and role of all personnel who manage, perform and verify work affecting quality.

Delegate in writing, authority to stop or reject work and the power to take action to prevent repetition.

Administer

Ensure that the personnel noted above have the necessary experience, qualifications or have received appropriate training commensurate with the responsibility and role undertaken.

Control

Appoint or nominate a management representative with defined authority and responsibility for ensuring that the requirements of the Quality System are implemented and maintained.

Regularly review the system at specified intervals to ensure its continuing effectiveness.

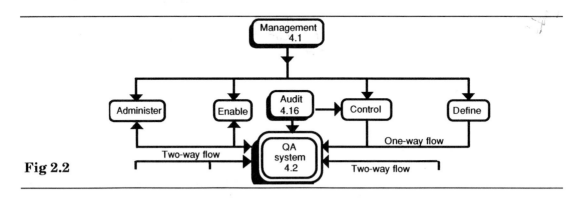

Fig 2.2

The diagram shows that management is directed via the Quality System, which management establishes and maintains via regular feedback. Control is exercised via Audit Procedures, see 2.2.10 later, which is a two-way process of continual improvement for the Quality System.

2.2.2 QA system (Clause 4.2)

- The System must be defined in a document.

- The document must be available to all personnel who have defined roles and responsibilities within it.

- The document must define the organisational structure, responsibilities, processes and resources applicable to ensuring that the project conforms to the specified requirements.

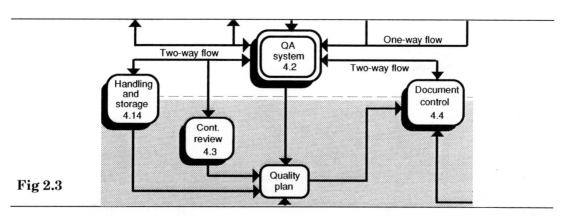

Fig 2.3

The diagram shows the QA system at its heart with its constituent elements feeding both to and from it. In a construction organisation the system exists at two levels. At company level are those processes and procedures which management require to be common to the whole organisation. At project level are the specific processes and procedures to operate in the unique circumstances of the project. The system must firstly be well planned and managed and secondly must produce documentary evidence of its existence and effective use. The Quality Plan is a vital element of the system but need only be as detailed as the complexities of each particular project demands. The Quality Manual is in effect a description of the way an organisation conducts its business.

Authors' note
  In practice the document too exists at two levels:

1. *The Quality Manual which will define the system and will be generally applicable to all relevant projects and operates at both company and project level.*
2. *The Quality Plan which BS 4778 defines as a document setting out the specific quality practices, resources and sequence of activities relevant to a particular project and operates specific to that project in conjunction with the Quality Manual.*

2.2.3 Contract review (Clause 4.3)

A procedure must be included at both Tender and Pre-Commencement Stages to review the client's requirements and:

1. Ensure that they are adequately defined, specified and documented.
2. Define and resolve any ambiguities or contradictions.
3. Ensure that resources are available.
4. Document the results of the above.

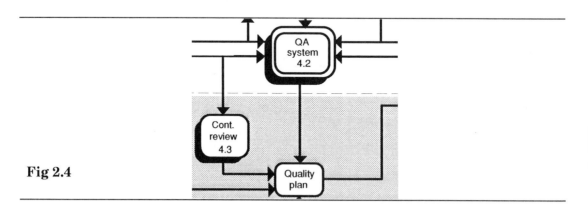

Fig 2.4

The diagram shows that the procedures to be adopted within the review noted above are defined within the system. Also that the documented results specific to the project are a necessary element to assist in the compilation of the Quality Plan. The process is intended to provide a clear recorded definition of each party's intentions or requirements at an early stage of the project.

Authors' note

This procedure is essential to the proper preparation of an effective Quality Plan. It also assists all parties in the identification of design / construction related problems at an early stage when experience suggests an amicable solution can often more easily be agreed.

2.2.4 Document control (Clause 4.4)

Procedures must be included to ensure that all drawings, specifications and other quality related documents, including revisions, are properly controlled.

Drawing and other registers must be kept up to date and record to whom copies have been distributed.

Procedures should be included to prevent the use of out of date information.

The procedures should extend to the control of information feedback in the form of Quality Records.

Fig 2.5

The main diagram illustrates the position of document control as we believe it should be used. The QA system establishes the procedures to be used and the Document Control system feeds those records relevant to the maintenance of the system back to the system to be available for inspection and audit. These records also assist management in its task of pursuing the continual improvement of the QA system noted in Clause 4.1.

Authors' note

The control of documentation is central to the effectiveness of a quality system and will provide a major source of information for audits of the system. This control is ensured by:

1. *Responsible personnel being identified.*
2. *The distribution being defined and recorded.*
3. *The documents themselves being adequately referenced so that they can be traced and identified.*

2.2.5 Purchasing (Clause 4.5)

Procedures, graded in stringency to the importance of the purchased item, must ensure that bought-in resources comply with the specified requirements and that those providing them are competent. Such compliance may be judged by:

1. Assessment of their formal Quality System.
2. In-house records of previous achievement.
3. Formal internal assessment procedure for examination of physical or documentary evidence of past performance.
4. Provision for higher level of main contractor supervision and support of their quality standards.

Procedures should also be included for the continual reassessment of bought-in resources based upon performance.

Procedures must be included to ensure that client supplied services or products, including information, also comply with the appropriate quality standard. (Clause 4.6)

Also include procedures that enable the standards and sources of products incorporated within the works to be identified and traced. (Clause 4.7)

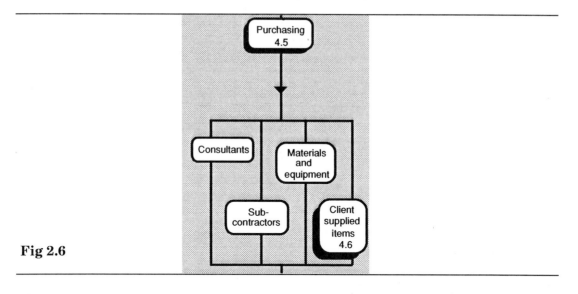

Fig 2.6

The diagram illustrates the nature of the resources to be purchased including those supplied by the client. The traceability element shown on the main diagram is fed back to the system via the quality records and document control.

Authors' note

Judgement must be used in applying these procedures and should be commensurate with the specified requirements or access for later inspection i.e. buried work may entail more stringent procedures than work which remains visible and open for inspection.

2.2.6 Process control (Clause 4.8)

Procedures must be included for:

- planning
- subsequent control
- documentation.

The procedures may be graded in rigour dependent upon judgement of the item's impact on quality.

Written method statements or instructions must be included where product quality would be affected if not used.

Intermediate stages must be defined, supervised, controlled and documented where work cannot be properly assessed in its final state.

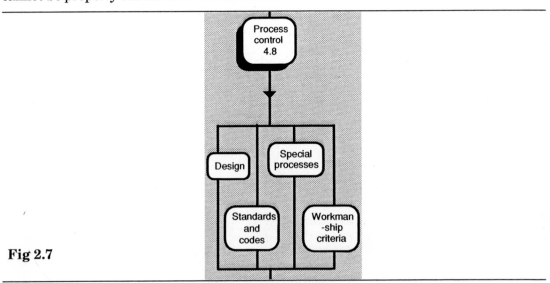

Fig 2.7

The main diagram shows Purchasing, Process Control and Inspection and Testing all feeding into the project specific Quality Plan. It is therefore within the Quality Plan that the documented project specific details of control of these elements will be produced. The excerpt above shows those elements of process control normally required to be catered for. Written method statements or instructions should be recorded within the Quality Records.

Authors' note

These items, where project specific, are identified within the Quality Plan. However where instructions or written method statements are required these could frequently take the form of standard checklists or procedures.

2.2.7 Inspection and testing (Clause 4.9)

Procedures must be included for:

- verification of compliance with specification. These must be produced at each of the following stages:
  1. upon receipt
  2. during construction
  3. at completion

- the routine checking and documentation of measuring and test equipment (Clause 4.10)

- the prevention of defective materials or workmanship being finally incorporated into the works through a system of instructions and records (Clause 4.11) and the control of non-conforming products (Clause 4.12)

- the implementation by management of corrective action in the event of non-conformance (Clause 4.13)

- the use of statistical techniques in establishing conformance (Clause 4.18).

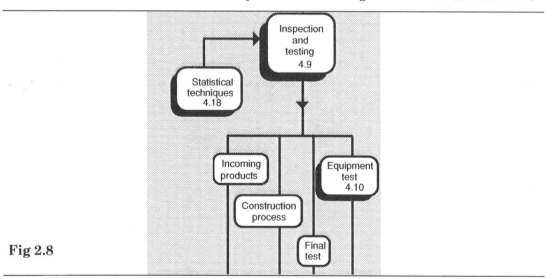

Fig 2.8

The main diagram links Statistical Techniques, Equipment Tests, Inspection and Test status and Non-conformance control within the area of Inspection and Testing. All of these elements would form part of the Quality Plan and the procedures for its preparation are given special consideration within Chapter 9.

Authors' note

The use of statistical techniques within this British Standard when applied to construction would normally be extremely limited e.g. to establish the necessary frequency of concrete cube tests.

2.2.8 Handling and storage (Clause 4.14)

Procedures must be included for:

- receipt of materials

- identification of materials

- inspection of materials

- handling and storage of materials in accordance with the manufacturers' recommendations to ensure protection from damage or deterioration

- protection of completed work until handover.

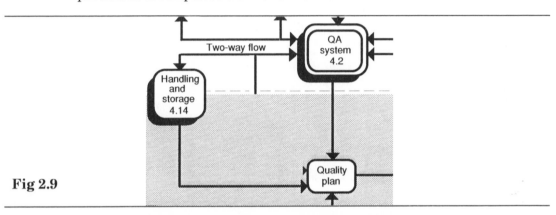

Fig 2.9

The diagram indicates that a number of the above procedures will be common to all projects but that particular circumstances may well require project specific procedures which would then be identified and written down within the Quality Plan.

Authors' note

Provision should be made within the procedures to prevent the use of materials which have exceeded their shelf life and thus the inspection of materials noted above must include periodic inspection of stored materials.

2.2.9 Quality records (Clause 4.15)

Records must be maintained, safely stored and be accessible for verification that work has been carried out in conformance with the quality system.

The degree of documentation and retention times of records shall be that agreed with the client or defined within the Quality System.

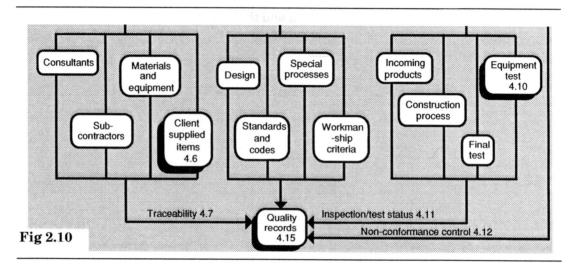

Fig 2.10

The diagram illustrates the wide variety of sources from which the Quality Records are required to be drawn. Any meaningful system must aim to make full use of these records as they form an important element of the feedback necessary for management's role in the continuous improvement and upgrading of the Quality System.

Authors' note

The records kept should be sufficient in terms of type and extent to demonstrate the required achievement of quality and should include pertinent subcontractors' quality records.

2.2.10 Audit (Clause 4.16)

A planned sequence of internal audits must be defined to ensure the effectiveness of the quality system.

This is a formal procedure by a delegated properly trained individual independent of the project structure and reporting directly to senior management.

The results of audits should be documented and the records should indicate deficiencies, corrective action and its timing and the person responsible for such action.

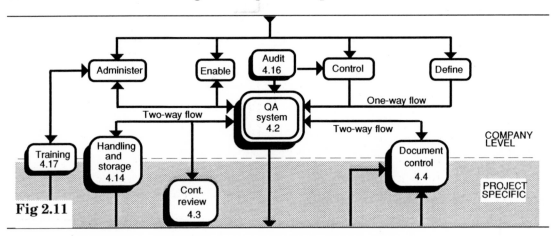

Fig 2.11

The diagram shows audit as the means of management control via the QA system and in particular the Quality Records fed back via document control to that system. It must be remembered that the audit is concerned with the operation of the system; the responsibility for ensuring that the required quality standards are attained, through use and improvement of the system, rests with management at all levels.

Another function of audit not clear from the diagram is to check the adequacy of training.

Authors' note

Such audits would be independent of a third party certifier; however records of their occurrence and any remedial action taken would be maintained and would provide evidence of the system's effectiveness.

2.2.11 Training (Clause 4.17)

Procedures must be included to ensure that:

- personnel records are kept and are available to confirm that staff or operatives requiring particular skills have been trained, tested or otherwise checked
- provision is made for additional training where a general or specific need is identified
- provision is made for quality awareness training
- particular attention is given to new personnel.

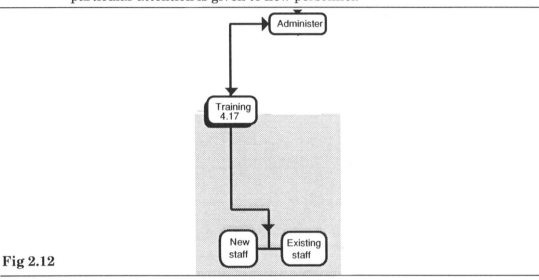

Fig 2.12

The diagram shows management's direct input into the improvement of what is undoubtedly its most important long term resource. The development of this resource concerns management at all levels of the organisation. Procedures for training, although primarily operating company wide, can also be project specific if the needs of a project introduce particular training requirements.

The next chapter describes in general terms how you would implement a quality assurance system within a construction organisation.

3.0   Generally

Looking at the synopsis in Chapter 2 it can be seen that the BS even when interpreted provides only a skeletal outline of the basic features that a complying QA system must provide. The difficulty then arises in applying these broad aims across a wide spectrum of activities and ensuring that the means are provided for their control. Regardless of the solution found, the process of implementation will pass through distinct stages. The three identified are:

- investigation
- development
- testing

Although these stages often overlap.

In practice there is also a less definable fourth stage of instigation. This stage commences with a realisation of the need for the management of quality within an organisation and concludes when a decision to proceed with a quality system is taken. At some point there is a crossover from instigation to investigation and although often the activities can run in parallel, it is preferable that a firm decision to produce a QA system be taken prior to the commencement of the investigation stage.

On conclusion of the instigation stage it is necessary to decide on the type of quality assurance system the company requires, and as previously mentioned there are three distinct options available:

First party certified

The company defines and polices its own quality system and thus has more control over its content and operation. A major disadvantage is that the system generally lacks credibility.

Second party certified

A company's quality system is approved and policed by the other party to the Contract. This can be a problem for companies operating with a large number of clients and also for clients who have to assess each individual contractor's system. Examples of client organisations that have operated such systems are the former Central Electricity Generating Board, British Nuclear Fuels Ltd. and various petro-chemical companies.

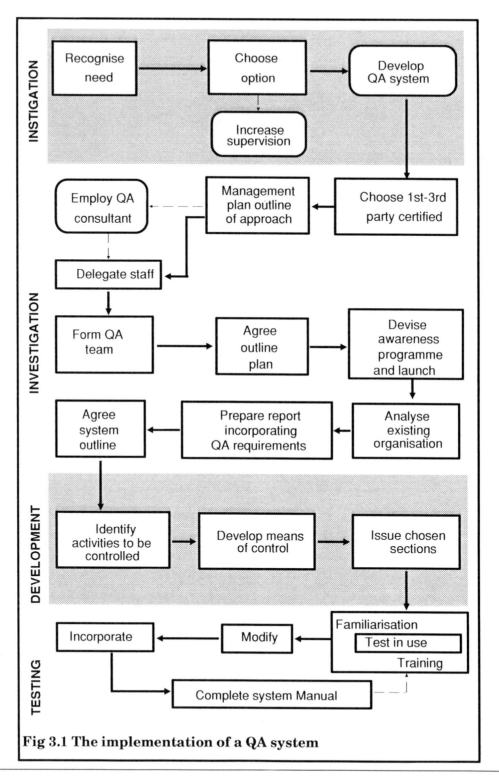

Fig 3.1 The implementation of a QA system

Third party certified

The system is authorised, checked and audited by an independent body allowing the company less control over its content and operation but ensuring discipline and credibility. Accredited Certification Bodies are listed on page 38.

Whichever system is developed it can, if desired, be restricted to operate within a part of the company's activities only, although as noted previously for third party certified systems, that part must be a significant portion of the company's activities.

Timescale

The implementation of any QA system will involve steps similar to those shown in Fig 3.1. A by-product of the system's use is improvement and therefore change which means that the last four steps contained in the Testing stage must follow a cyclical process.

A minimum period for the implementation of the initial system would probably be nine to twelve months.

3.1   Instigation

As previously discussed this initial stage commences with a perceived need to assure the achievement of quality. Next there is an examination of the options available. As stated in Chapter 1 the choice lies between increasing supervision and the implementation of a quality system. Once a decision to produce a QA system is taken the process passes from the instigation to the investigation stage.

3.2   Investigation

The first step at this stage is to decide the grade of system to be produced. The choice is a system that satisfies either:

- the company's internal requirements (1st Party)
- a particular customer's requirements (2nd party)
- all potential customers' requirements (3rd party).

Having decided this it is necessary to plan in outline an approach suitable to the company's particular circumstances. The next decision is whether to employ a QA Consultant. It is worth noting that a government grant is available to most organisations for part of the cost. Alternatively the choice may be to handle the entire process in-house (note the continuum Fig 1.3).

Having thereby formed the QA team they, together with management, must then agree the plan for the balance of the investigation, development and testing stages of the system.

A quality awareness programme should be planned and implemented. This programme is intended to notify all staff of the company's objectives and should be designed to provide reassurance and foster their continuing support during the three phases of its implementation.

Various methods can be used but it is essential to emphasise top management's total commitment by for example their presence at a launch gathering of personnel at some special venue. The aim must be to give this process a high internal profile from the very start.

Following the company's launch the implementation of the next three stages may then proceed.

3.2.1 Analyse existing organisation

In our opinion it is fundamental for the long term success of the system that it be developed as an integral part of the company's existing procedures. As a pre-requisite to this development it is therefore essential to examine the company in great detail in terms of its organisation and procedures.

For this process there are at least three methods which can be used:

- firstly, self analysis by section/department heads and their staff
- secondly, analysis by QA Manager (or similar) appointed within the company
- thirdly, analysis by external consultants.

Each method has particular advantages and disadvantages (see Fig 1.3). We believe that a combination of all three can maximise the advantages and minimise the disadvantages of each, producing a blend of understanding of QA with a detailed knowledge of the organisation's activities.

This analysis may appear to be an unnecessary exercise as every organisation will already have a detailed knowledge of what it does. However, the company's perception of its organisation and structure will on closer examination normally prove false.

Typically this examination will reveal:

- titles and positions that often do not match the actual roles undertaken
- procedures that in practice are frequently ignored or modified for a variety of reasons
- procedures that are frequently out of date or contradict other stated principles within the same or other documents.

A company's organisation and procedures have often been developed on an ad hoc basis and the introduction of a QA System has the additional benefit of providing the opportunity to rationalise the whole.

The introduction of a quality assurance system enables a company to undertake a critical review of current or previous methods of working, and is of itself often a process of improvement.

In examining this actual structure you must show roles and responsibilities, methods of control, routes of information flow and the means by which these operate.

To gain this information the following means may be used:

- structured interviews using a standard format of questions that will produce or confirm the information required
- questionnaires again using the standard format but questions must be unambiguous
- study of documentary evidence enabling comparison to be made between what has been said and what has happened.

Information via these methods will need to be gathered from all areas of the company including central support departments, project teams, company manuals and a detailed examination of records of current and past projects.

Interviews

These may be appropriate for senior or key personnel and they have the advantages of:

1. Guaranteeing a prompt response to your enquiry.
2. Giving an opportunity to ask secondary or follow up questions if the response is unclear.
3. Assuring and relaxing the person answering who is more likely to open up.
4. Assisting in the development of the questionnaire.

The obvious disadvantage is the time commitment of both interviewer and interviewee.

Questionnaires

They will normally follow interviews (see 4. above) and may be targeted to junior or subsidiary personnel. It is unlikely that a single questionnaire will be appropriate to all employees, so modified versions may have to be produced for specific groups or individuals although the central core of information is likely to remain the same. Questionnaires have the advantages of concurrence of completion and time saving for interviewers. However the disadvantages almost mirror the advantages of interviewing:

1. They need following up to get both a complete and prompt response - it helps if responsibility for ensuring this is given to their superior following that person's interview. A timescale for completion must be given.
2. The questions must be as clear and unambiguous as possible- a pilot exercise is advisable.
3. It helps if they are returned in pre-marked sealed envelopes and some confidentiality is provided.

If the information so provided is found to be of interest or raises further questions this can then be followed through by means of an interview.

Not all responses will be accurate and the information will need to be checked. The spread of responses will enable development of the general pattern of information required.

Study of documentary evidence

This is the final source of information and is most useful to fill in gaps or check the accuracy of other information. It is also likely that information from two sources will conflict; these conflicts are often best resolved by bringing both sources together and discussing the problems which may only be a matter of perception or interpretation.

It is however important during this stage to take care to avoid alienating any individuals as support for the process will continually need to be fostered.

Following analysis of this information, conclusions will be developed and a report prepared and submitted to senior management.

3.2.2 Prepare report incorporating QA amendments

The report

Its contents should be drawn in part from the investigator's conclusions, but should clearly express the opinions and observations of the staff.

The report is likely to outline the following:

- the company's present structure
- the roles and responsibilities of departments and staff
- the company's organisation and methods of control
- difficulties and problems highlighted with particular relevance to divergences from the company's expected structure, roles and organisation
- a particular section related to missing or poorly addressed areas of the British Standard and possible options to address these deficiencies
- a proposed programme for future development.

Structure of the organisation

The structure is likely to develop similarly for all project based companies with a large degree of responsible autonomy at site management level. An example of an extract of a simple structure diagram is shown in Fig 3.2 opposite. Names and information flows would be added to this diagram to provide the detail necessary.

Some typical problems which can be observed from a **detailed** diagram may be:

1. The geographic division of some individuals' workload may lead to excessive time spent in travelling, thereby reducing their effectiveness and creating paper roles that cannot exist in practice.
2. Larger than planned quantities of work in strategic areas falling to individuals with dual roles, where competing demands upon their time result either in delay or insufficient attention.
3. Lack of clarity or understanding of roles means that communication lines in some instances by-pass the formal management structure.
4. Middle management often have too wide an authority with poorly defined responsibility.

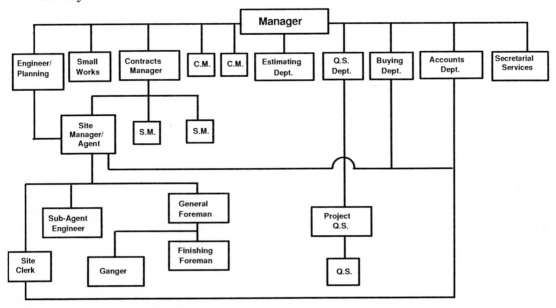

Fig 3.2 Structure diagram

Roles and responsibilities

The following typical points may be highlighted.

Support departments Central support department staff tend to have well defined roles within the department; however their external authority and responsibility is often poorly defined.

Estimating Typical problems may be that:

1. Staff are subject to a generally heavy though variable workload which means that tenders sometimes suffer in terms of depth of input and thus quality.
2. Data banks of suppliers and subcontractors are often incomplete and relate heavily to cost (or the ability to return tenders) rather than a balance of cost and quality.

3. Variable or unstructured feedback of information from sites allows the continued use of incorrect data.
4. The experience and availability of site staff leads to wide variations in the extent and quality of their input into tenders.

Quantity surveying Typical problems may be:

1. The amount of time and resources devoted to financial reporting from which projects may gain very little in terms of useful feedback.
2. Problems in reconciling tender allowances from data provided.
3. The time consumed in dealing with large numbers of subcontractors.

Personnel department Typical problems may be:

1. Deficiencies in their records of individuals' past experience and the absence of proof of qualifications.
2. Lack of access to records for site based management.
3. Incompatibility of knowledge of interviewer with the skills of interviewee leads to inappropriate appointments.

Site based personnel Particular roles below that of Site Agent will be largely at the discretion of the site manager. However there is often confusion at site level when they attempt to define the exact extent of their roles and responsibilities.

Typical problems may be:

1. That because of this lack of definition scope exists for work to be duplicated, poorly addressed or even missed altogether.
2. Titles and roles do not always match, leading to problems when staff are transferred.
3. The support necessary for individuals carrying out the same roles will vary considerably.
4. Individuals with a professional or academic base will express differing needs to those with a practical base and perceive their roles from widely differing viewpoints.
5. Project teams will in some instances tend to lack balance between experience and expertise.

Organisation

Company manuals tend to grow without regard to their usability and thus the processes and procedures that staff frequently use will often be found to be ad hoc developments of what is actually required. Because of this variability management control is often illusory.

Typical problems for site managers from existing organisational methods and control could be:

1. Shortage of time at commencement of a contract leading to an early use of reactive rather than proactive measures which are often a continuing source of problems demanding further time.
2. Inconsistency in transfer of information to site teams - leading to a slower than necessary understanding of the project.
3. Lack of time for supervision - stemming from:

   - shortage of time at commencement

   - poor information flow both internal and external

   - lack of support increasing workload

   - inappropriate proportion of time spent on providing historic cost information.

4. Frequently because of the power of central management, organisations tend to demand information from projects but lack procedures for exchanging information, creating an imbalance which may lead to a breakdown in communication.

3.2.3 Report format

It is worth remembering that the people that will be required to read and understand this report are often pressed for time so make it concise.

As part of this report flow charts can be used as an aid to graphically identify the involvement of both individuals and departments within the process of completing a project. See Fig 3.3.

Having defined firstly the system required and secondly the company's structure, roles and organisation, actual rather than assumed, it should be possible to identify divergences, contradictions and most importantly missing areas.

From this information a schedule, as previously noted, can be prepared identifying the divergences between the company's current procedures and those necessary for the proposed quality system. Within the report the schedule may offer alternatives as to how these divergences can be answered. See Fig 3.4.

Fig 3.3 Report flowchart extract

EXISTING	MISSING	OPTIONS

Contract review
 	
* Pre-construction meeting with client
 	
* Varying appraisal depending upon site staff availability
	* Standardised and resourced appraisal procedures
	
	* Structured and documented arrangement for meetings
		* Formalise existing procedures
		
		* Resources:
		    *appoint new staff
		    *accommodate wider role by modifying existing duties
		    *combination of above

Fig 3.4 Extract of schedule of missing and incomplete procedures, resources and documents related to BS requirements

3.2.4 Agree system outline

Management's response to the report in the form of observations and choices should enable an outline of the proposed system to be agreed.

The report and management's response provide a basis for understanding the order of tasks and integration of both individuals and departments within the company's system and would therefore form a starting point for the development of a QA System.

3.3   Development

The initial flow charts developed for the report together with any management comments should be sent to each department or project and staff asked to comment and expand upon them. From their response a revised flow chart can be prepared and returned to the departments for further comment. Interfaces and processes which are still unclear or contradictory can then resolved by joint discussion, normally by bringing dissenting parties face to face.

Rudyard Kipling wrote a story called the Elephant's Child. In it he referred to six stalwart serving men who served him well and true. He called them What, Why, When, How, Where and Who. A good quality system, in our opinion, must provide these six servants in order for the system to serve the company well:

- defining what is to be done
- explaining why it is done
- establishing when it is to be done
- controlling how it is to be done
- showing where it is done
- identifying who is to do it.

The system thus developed should contain not only the quality related procedures but also dovetail into existing systems of administration, accountability and control. The principle is to set down the system within a main reference document that also has all other company documents referred and subsidiary to it. One solution to achieving this is discussed in detail over the next five chapters.

3.4   Testing

Sections of the system should be introduced progressively on a selective basis. If problems then occur they can be amended to remove the ambiguity or unnecessary item or add any missing points. The system will thereby become refined in use before actually being completed. Upon completion of all stages the documents are brought together combining the requirements of the British Standard with references to the company's own

---

procedures. This will eventually form the principle part of the QA Manual referred to in the next chapter.

Having completed the system it will be necessary to get approval of the whole and to agree a progressive programme of familiarisation and training in the use of the new procedures. The means of maintaining the system should be defined within the system itself. However it must be accepted that the system through use, particularly in its reporting and auditing procedures, will undergo continuous amendment and improvement.

From the commencement of this process you must keep in mind that the system you are producing will, if it is properly used, be subject to continual improvement. See Fig 3.5.

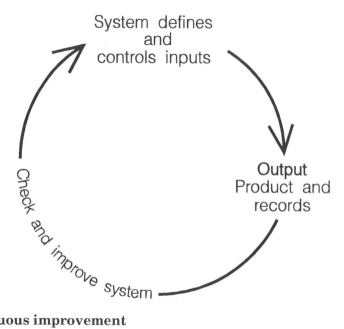

Fig 3.5 Continuous improvement

The use of audits, discussed in Chapter 9, must focus on the procedures and their effectiveness. Effectiveness should be judged, in this context, by the achievement of quality. If quality is consistently achieved without adherence to particular procedures, then the procedures may be unnecessary or incorrect. The aim is not to produce a paper chase but procedures that ensure that quality is achieved.

We believe the system outlined in the following chapters provides a basis to achieve this. However it is worth emphasising that the company's staff should feel involved in the whole process described above and feel of the system 'they did it all themselves'. What we would describe as 'the sense of property' thereby generated will ease the harnessing of their support and help ensure a positive attitude in applying the system.

Remember before designing your system not only what your aims are but also what you must seek to avoid.

Your system should not:

1. inhibit positive innovation
2. feel an imposition
3. be difficult to use

Your system should:

1. assist real tasks not dictate superfluous detail
2. make good sense
3. be theirs

Solutions to the points noted are many and various but the remainder of this book provides one solution and some of the reasons for its development.

The next chapter describes the QA Manual and its method of operation.

Relevant accredited Certification Bodies include:

British Standards Institute,
Quality Assurance Service
PO Box 375
Milton Keynes MK14 6LL

Lloyds Register Quality Assurance
Norfolk House
Wellesley Road
Croydon   CR9 2DT

Yarsley Quality Assured Firms Ltd
Trowers Way
Redhill
Surrey   RH1 2JN

4.0   Structure of the system developed

Having talked about QA systems in general we shall now go on to consider the system developed from our own work and its method of operation. This we believe could form a framework for the development of your own system.

Fig 4.1 on page 41 shows the index for a QA Manual illustrating our solution highlighting the necessary component parts. Note that the Manual is divided into five main sections with subdivisions where appropriate.

4.0.1 The main sections

Section 1 The director's statement

Clause 4.1 requires that management must define in the form of a written statement its policy, objectives and commitment. This statement must be published throughout the organisation and be seen as supported by management. Clients should also be made aware of this policy.

Policy may be described as a broad statement of the company's aims. Objectives are the means by which the policy may be implemented and should be perceived both as achievable and measurable. Commitment means that management is fully behind the policy and objectives.

The obvious place for the publication of the director's statement is the Quality Manual where it forms the introduction. Typical examples are published by the CIOB, BEC and other organisations but a further example is given in Fig 4.5 on page 48.

Section 2 Control systems for manual

Clause 4.2 requires that the system be defined in a document and that the document must be available to all personnel who have defined roles and responsibilities within it.

It is therefore necessary to produce and circulate copies of the Manual within the organisation. Clause 4.1 requires management to regularly review the system to ensure its continuing effectiveness. It is a necessary virtue of an effective appraisal that improvements will have to be made and thus changes to the documentation will be necessary.

Therefore an effective control of these documents will be required. This control has a number of purposes:

1. To record that everyone who is required to have a copy of the Manual has received one.
2. To ensure that any sundry amendments to the Manual are identifiable and circulated to the holders of the Manuals.
3. To ensure that amendments are approved by management prior to their incorporation.

For the purpose of item one it is necessary that a person is given responsibility for developing a circulation policy and drafting and maintaining a list of those persons to whom the copies are to be issued.

The purpose of item two requires that the document must be produced identifying individual pages by means of a discrete reference. The circulation of amendments to any pages should also be controlled and recorded. See example below:

QA MANUAL	Notes	SECTION	Company Procedures		
		STAGE	Tender		
		REF	QAM 4		T/1
		REV		DATE	
		SHEET	1	of	22

REF	QAM 4 indicates that the page is within Section 4 of the QA manual.
T/1	Shows that it is the first page of the Tender stage.
REV	Allows revisions to be enumerated and the date of their issue entered.
SHEET	Shows that it is part of a sequence of 22 sheets.

The purpose of item three is to avoid documents being amended on an ad hoc basis; therefore a procedure for authorising amendments must be specified.

Section 3 Company organisation chart

Clause 4.2 requires that the document defines the organisational structure of the company. It is in the nature of project based organisations that their organisational structure will undergo continual changes as existing projects end and new projects start. In satisfying this part of the British Standard it is advisable to consider the organisation in two tiers:

- Tier 1 - the relatively stable central administrative organisation
- Tier 2 - the project based organisation.

The first tier is best developed within this section of the Manual. The second tier is project specific and is best developed within the Quality Plan (see chapter 8). This can then be related in terms of its interfaces and links back to the company organisation chart. The main advantages of doing this are:

- it avoids constant amendment to the manual
- the charts in each Quality Plan are limited to those relevant to each project's staff.

	QA MANUAL INDEX	
Section		Book Reference
1.	Director's statement	Chapter 4
2.	Control system for Manual	Chapter 4
3.	Company organisation chart	Chapter 4
4.	Company procedures	Chapter 4
	1. Staged procedures	
	1.1 Tender stage - Sheets T/1-T/22	Chapter 5
	1.2 Mobilisation stage - Sheets M/1-M/2	Chapter 6
	1.3 Construction stage - Sheets C/1-C/10	Chapter 7
	2. General procedures	
	2.1 Document control ✓	Chapter 8
	2.2 Enquiry ✓	
	2.3 Ordering ✓	
	2.4 Quality plan	Chapter 8
	2.5 Material, delivery and handling	
	2.6 Quantity Surveyors ✓	
	2.7 Audit ✓	Chapter 9
	2.8 Recruitment / training ✓	Chapter 9
5.	Supporting documentation	
	1. Forms QA/A - QA/Y	Chapter 10
	2. Works guidance notes	
	3. Job descriptions	

Fig 4.1 QA Manual index

Section 4 Company procedures

BS 5750 : Part 4 : 1990 in its definition of the Quality Manual states that *Any planned system should be documented and recorded and should form the basis for a quality manual which becomes a description of the way the organisation conducts its business.* This description of the way the organisation works therefore is the core of any QA system.

In describing the company's activities the report produced from the investigation was drawn from different groups at different stages of the project. Therefore it seemed appropriate to subdivide the system into these same stages of tender, mobilisation and construction. In analysing activities some were found to be discrete to a particular stage and others spanned a number of these stages. In addition certain tasks needed a lengthy explanation which tended to detract from the main flow of information. Therefore company procedures were divided into those that could be accommodated in staged procedures and the other tasks which spanned stages or needed detailed explanation; the latter were separated and called General Procedures. Both of these will be illustrated in some detail in Chapters 5 to 8.

Section 5 Supporting documentation

Noted within Chapters 5 to 8 are documents referred to on the index as Supporting Documentation.

The first documents are the Forms which have the function of expanding the information given and also act as live documents within the system. Completion of the forms is part of the procedures within the system and their storage and inspection constitutes a key element in the maintenance and control of the system.

Secondly there are Works Guidance Notes which are an aid to site management. These highlight standard activities and hold points for typical operations found within project Quality Plans (examples are shown within the Quality Plan Procedures pages 118-119).

Job descriptions are the final documents, although as described in the Quality Plan Procedures, these are standard job descriptions which may be subject to written amendment.

4.1   Philosophy of the system developed

The system developed is applicable to a construction organisation's building operations in accordance with BS 5750 : Part 2 : 1987 (ISO 9002, EN 29002) with a view to obtaining third party certification.

It is a basic premise of quality systems that to control the quality of work, means must be introduced to control the inputs into that work. It is arguable as to what depth a system needs to go. Construction involves a wide variety of inputs all with a mutitude of facets occurring over a series of often remote stages. It is therefore difficult to decide how insignificant or remote, from the final product, a task needs to be before control is no longer required. This system has tended in some respects to take this need to what some will consider to be extremes. For instance does the quality of the tender affect the final quality of the constructed building. Research indicates that it does.

Consider the following management problems of time, information, resources and control which are found to be present in varying degrees at all stages of a project.

Typically:

Stage	Problems			
Tender	Time pressure variable	Information missing	Resources variable	Control O.K.
Mobilisation	Time pressure variable	Information missing	Resources variable	Control difficult
Construction	Time periodically	Information periodically	Resources periodically	Control difficult
Defects	Time O.K.	Information O.K.	Resources short	Control variable

Whilst time pressures during the construction stage are sometimes variable it is common in today's industry for the time constraints to be a critical factor from the commencement of many projects. It is at this commencement point that the failings of the processes leading up to the construction stage start to appear. The resolution of these failings will then rob a frequently overstretched site management team of further time. Attention to detail in preparing tenders and setting up a project ensures a maximum use of available time and resources to provide a vitally important platform for a successful project.

This is not to say that from a quality point of view, if this situation should exist by the construction stage, it is irretrievable. However the methods used in retrieving the situation will often affect the balance of time, cost and quality and the contractor is unfortunately faced with having to sacrifice one or two aspects of this eternal triangle.

Another reason for the system having to be developed in some detail is that the British Standard specifically requires you to ascertain, prior to submitting your tender, the client's requirements. A contractor should not passively or knowingly accept incomplete or incorrect information on the basis that this is the client's or others' problem. It is recognised that the quality of what is received is often beyond control. However the processes of seeking and identifying what is needed, within reason and within the constraints of the constructor's role, must be provided for within the QA system.

For both these reasons it is necessary to investigate and develop flow charts of the tender and mobilisation stages in some detail.

It will be noted in the next three chapters that frequent meetings are called for. This is not a requirement of the British Standard but is a useful management tool. It assists in co-ordinating and ensuring that tasks are addressed at the correct stage and that there is a general appreciation by the team of where they are going. These meetings will often be short and relatively informal. They will provide a forum which enables all those with responsibility to communicate or appreciate problems at the earliest possible time.

4.2   The system developed

The system to be produced must incorporate Rudyard Kipling's six servants i.e. the what, when, who, where, how and why of the company's activities. These may be established as follows.

From the distilled information of the investigation it is possible to define **what** is to be done, **when** it is done and **who** does it. Alternative flows caused by varying project types may be discovered and eventually separate processes, each with varying degrees of communality, will be identified. From these alternatives the **where** will be established.

Strategic points along the flow charts can then be identified and a means of control, by the use of checklists and detailed procedures (**how**), developed. Finally in order to obtain a consistency of roles, standard job descriptions written to interface with the flow charts, notes and procedures previously described, can be developed. The job descriptions emphasise the philosophy of the work to be undertaken rather than prescribe a didactic schedule of tasks. The junior positions require more detailed notes on how to undertake particular job-specific tasks although the majority of these may be covered using forms or general procedures.

The system thus emerging consists of a central flow chart of activities highlighting individual responsibilities supported by explanatory notes (**why**) and forms, these forms thereby acting as an expansion of the flow chart providing agendas or checklists at strategic points. In addition detailed procedures on particular activities can be prepared and referenced either on the flow chart or within the forms.

The system therefore consists of:

1.   The central flow charts trace the core activities in some detail.
2.   The signposting on the flow charts establishes responsibility for tasks.
3.   The explanatory notes on or adjacent to the flow charts provide guidance and expand the detail of the task.
4.   The forms referred to in the flow chart or notes provide a deeper insight into the detail of the task, amounting almost to a step by step guide as well as acting as a permanent record.
5.   The general procedures describe general tasks in detail to ensure their execution in a uniform manner.
6.   The job descriptions explain management's perspective of the general nature of the role the individual is expected to undertake.

Any system must have a core or starting point and whilst much of what is shown on the flow chart or forms may appear to be simplistic, our research has shown that they are frequently the very points which are missed or poorly addressed. We start therefore from the viewpoint of taking nothing for granted.

Looking at an extract taken from Page T/6 (book page 59) of the tender stage of the flow chart:

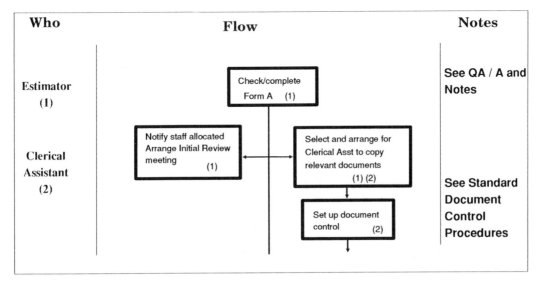

Fig 4.2 Extract from Tender Stage flow chart

The columns are headed Who, Flow and Notes. The Flow column is the core of the system, the boxes describing tasks, generally in the order of their execution, and indicating by means of a numbered key the person or persons responsible for ensuring the tasks are undertaken. The Who column provides a permanently visible responsibility key. The Notes column will normally direct that person to a more detailed explanation either on the facing page or elsewhere in the manual.

For example the relevant facing page for Page T/6 (Fig 4.3 below) describes the nature of the task in completing any missing sections on Form QA/A designed to set out the basic enquiry information. The forms themselves are listed alphabetically and are kept within the Supporting Documentation section of the Manual. The forms are designed to be used to provide permanent records and as such become part of the company's standard stationery.

> ❏ **Form QA/A (cont'd)**
> The Estimator checks the form and adds any missing information. A copy of the form is to be filed in the 'Records Section' of the Main/Tender/Contract file as part of the document control procedures by the Clerical Assistant. See Document Control Procedures.

Fig 4.3 Notes from facing page T/6

Reference is also made to Document Control procedures. This and other General procedures are included for complex tasks peripheral to the main flow of activities and are included within Section 4.2 of the Manual.

So within the short extract of the flow chart shown in Fig 4.2:

1. The Estimator has

- checked and/or completed the form which will provide a permanent record of the Tender details (such details must therefore have been considered at this stage)
- selected the documents to be issued to other staff involved
- set up the first meeting for the team. The philosophy of the meeting (which is shown below at Fig 4.4) is described later in the flow through Form QA/E which also acts as an agenda.

2. Management has

- defined how keenly the company is viewing the tender at this point in time
- decided what staff are allocated to the tender.

3. The Clerical Assistant has

- filed the form in the records section of the appropriate file
- copied appropriate documents for staff
- set up the Document Control procedures - use of codes, format of files.

❏ **Form QA/E Initial Review Meeting**
The purpose behind the meeting is to establish at an early stage:

1. The formation of a project team.
2. The agreement of a tender timetable.
3. An appreciation of the adequacy of the tender information.
4. An outline of the method and organisation envisaged.
5. The allocation of tasks to members of the team.

The form provides a basic agenda and acts as part of a permanent record of the initial decisions taken. It also ensures that some of the questions required for the Contract Review meeting with the client are established at an early date.

Fig 4.4 Notes for Form QA/E

If you refer to the Form QA/E on page 136 it will indicate how the above philosophy is addressed in a practical manner.

The system is therefore aiming to cover the tasks in great detail whilst keeping them in linked but manageable portions like the layers of a sandwich cake. The conflict between providing forms which act as concise checklists and providing sufficient space for the entry of records has been catered for by allowing the attachment of further sheets which are to be referred to on the forms.

4.3   The operation of the system

Each individual with responsibility is required to have a copy of the QA Manual.

The order and responsibility for all the significant tasks undertaken are followed by means of the flow charts. The points of control are those that have forms to be completed or meetings to be held and recorded. The forms and agendas have the additional function of expanding the areas which management require to be consistently addressed.

The completion of the forms and the additional detail from the meetings provide a permanent record that the tasks have been addressed. Should there be any future problems then the source of the problem should be traceable.

The system therefore:

- provides guidance for the individual
- control for the manager
- assurance for the client.

A more detailed explanation of the operation of this section of the Manual can be found on page 54 which shows the actual guidance notes incorporated within the Manual.

The production of a system heavily dependent upon graphic forms and flow charts requires that such documents should be capable of amendment within the organisation. It is therefore advisable, where possible, to develop all material on a desk-top publishing system. By this means amendments can be easily and quickly incorporated both during development and future use of the system.

The next three chapters set out the system developed in detail, each chapter being prefaced with a brief explanation of the logic which led to the controls and procedures incorporated within each stage.

Chapter 8 looks in detail at procedures for preparing and maintaining Quality Plans and Document Control which are key elements in a QA system.

Our company's corporate purpose is to provide a quality service to our clients in providing their specified requirements. Only by so doing will we achieve our aims of sustained improvement and profitability.

It is my opinion that the use of this Quality Manual will greatly contribute to these aims.

All personnel within the company are individually responsible for the quality of their work. The procedures contained within this Manual are designed to assist all employees in ensuring that work for which they are responsible meets required standards.

The Quality Manager will monitor and report directly to me on the implementation and effectiveness of this Manual in achieving the above aims.

Signed   (Managing Director)

Date

Fig 4.5 Example of Director's statement

THE SYSTEM DEVELOPED - TENDER STAGE

5.0   The points addressed

The system developed for this stage addresses two principle issues:

- the BS requirements
- the specific problems discovered at the investigation stage.

The clauses of BS 5750 : Part 2 accounted for at this stage were:

4.1	Management
4.2	QA system
4.3	Contract review
4.4	Document control
4.5	Purchasing
4.8	Process control
4.15	Quality records
4.16	Audit
4.17	Training

Whilst the problems discovered were many and varied the major aspects occurred broadly in four areas:

- time availibility varied but tended to be limited to 4-6 weeks which was frequently inadequate
- resources were generally stretched and poorly distributed
- information was of variable quality but tended to be incomplete or inaccurate
- control tended to be good because the activities were systematically undertaken and checked but some problems existed.

5.1   Issues considered under the relevant BS headings

The two principle issues addressed are considered here jointly under the appropriate BS reference heading. The discussion thereby blends the necessary improvements to existing procedures with the requirements of the British Standard.

5.1.1 Management

Management's policy and objectives are defined within the director's statement previously noted in Chapter 4.

The fact that the BS requires it to be implemented from the top down places a discipline on **all** members of the organisation.

Time and resources were seen as particular problems which a management input could serve to solve. Some early decisions from management were incorporated as part of the system. The Enquiry Review (see diamond on flow chart T/4 page 57) requires the manager to classify the tender into one of four categories; depending upon this category the staffing level is established and the individuals named and allocated to the tender team.

Management must recognise the importance of allowing the estimator as much time as possible to maximise the use of resources early. The system provides a discipline which increases the time available on appropriate projects as the categorisation enables an appropriate level of resources to be directed earlier. Some tenders would receive a lower staff input thus freeing resources for projects in a higher category. Flexibility was also required and this was catered for in a controlled way.

This became an enabling process with the flow chart defining the responsibility and role for **all** staff.

Management's role in administration is reflected in the company's training policy. Control is provided for within the system and the responsibility is defined within the Audit procedures.

5.1.2 The QA system

The system is defined and the documents are available to the necessary personnel. The organisational structure at each stage is defined within various documents.

At this stage:

- staff - defined on Form QA/A (page 128)
- roles - are defined at the Initial Review meeting (see Flow Chart T/6 page 59 and Form QA/E page 136)
- processes - are defined by compliance with forms and general procedures.

5.1.3 Contract review

The BS requires the contractor to institute a procedure which examines, resolves and documents the process of ensuring that the client's specification is understood. Part of this process is to arrange a meeting with the client's representative. Whilst it is recognised that not all clients would wish to co-operate in such a process, it does provide the optimum solution. The meeting is shown on Flow Chart T/8 (page 61) and the agenda provided by Form QA/G (page 138). In addition processes of inspection and evaluation of information received are provided for, see Form QA/E (page 136).

5.1.4 Document control

Obtaining and documenting information is a problem at most stages of a project. A further difficulty is ensuring that everyone knows what information has been received, where it is and who has received it.

Document control is introduced at this stage using a modified version of the full Document Control procedures, see Flow Chart T/8 (page 61). Refer to Chapter 8 for more detail.

5.1.5 Purchasing

Time, resources and information normally mitigate against too extensive a procedure at this stage. However it is advisable to do all that is possible to ensure that the tender prices reflect the specified requirements. This is catered for within the Enquiry and Checking procedures on Forms QA/C (pages 131-132) and QA/F (page 137), see Flow Chart T/6 (page 59).

A difficult aspect of the BS was the requirement to ensure that client supplied services or products, including information, complied with the appropriate quality standard. Here it was decided not to extend the contractors' responsibility beyond the liability created by the duty of care.

5.1.6 Process control

The effective use of time and resources is critical at this stage, therefore process control can only receive limited attention. The involvement of available site staff and the planning engineer at this early stage should however enable some basic planning to enable completion of the Programme and Method Review Report on Form QA/B1 (page 129), see Flow Chart T/10 (page 63).

5.1.7 Quality records

The forms together with the implementation of the Document Control procedures are designed to answer this particular requirement.

5.1.8 Audit

The planned sequence of internal audits is defined within the Audit procedures and will depend to a large extent upon reference to the quality records provided by the system. Audits are thereby simplified by the use of Forms QA/A to QA/K relevant to this stage.

These provide an accessible and complete record which answers a large proportion of the auditor's questions. See Chapter 9 for more details.

5.1.9 Training

The selection of the best available staff is important even at this early stage. Detailed records of staff experience and training ensure that management are provided with the relevant information to aid this process. Two other factors are important. Firstly recruitment procedures must be tightened up. Secondly career structures for staff have to be developed and a system of monitoring them instigated. See Chapter 9 for more details.

❏ **A detailed edited extract of this section of the Manual follows.**

All pages with the QA Manual heading are taken directly from the Manual.

Authors' note

Whilst for completeness procedures for all categories of tender have been included, for ease of understanding you are advised initially to follow Category A procedures only (T/1 - T/12) and refer to Category D (T/22).

Subsequently you may wish to examine the alternative procedures for Categories B and C.

Notes for guidance in use of QA Manual

Tender Stage (QA Manual-Flow Charts Pages T/1 to T/22)

Generally

The flow chart plots the progress of a tender from receipt to submittal. The left hand column indicates and numbers the parties involved in the section of work covered by each page. The centre column traces the activities which are to be carried out and are numbered to indicate who does it. The right hand column refers you to forms, copies of which are to be found in Section 5.1 Forms, or are simply notes on how to proceed.

An example of how this manual should be used is as follows:-

All procedures start at Flow Chart QA Manual Page T/4 - refer now to this page.

The main sequence on the left hand side of the **centre** flow column are the company's procedures for receiving and recording tender documents. On the right hand side of the centre column a copy of the covering letter has gone to the Area Manager which ensures that he is aware of their receipt. *The initial tasks and the persons responsible are shown in the main sequence boxes.*

Closely following this receipt a decision is taken by the Area Manager and Area Estimator at the Enquiry Review concerning the company's interest in the tender and staff availability *(the diamond box indicates a decision point).*

During this stage Form QA/A should be completed by the Clerical Assistant giving all necessary background information on the tender, plus recording the decisions taken at the Enquiry Review.

For this example we are assuming the tender is a traditional one and the decision taken at the Enquiry Review has been to place it in Category B.

This means that because either the company is not sure of its interest or that staff are unavailable it will not receive at this initial stage the full input of resources demanded for Category A procedures.

The continuation of procedures for Category B are on flow chart Page T/14.

From this point the Estimator has responsibility for ensuring that all procedures are adhered to.

All forms noted in the right hand column must be completed.

The forms are read in conjunction with notes on the facing page to the flow chart. This enables completion of the form to a standard that produces a checklist of activities and ultimately a record of information and decisions taken.

If there is insufficient room within a section of the form please use continuation sheets but these must be cross-referenced at that section of the form.

Following Category B procedures through to Page T/16 after the Contract Review meeting with the client there is a diamond box where a further decision must be taken.

As can be seen on Notes to Page T/3 a decision to upgrade a Category B to A must not be made later than 2 weeks from the tender submittal date.

At this point a decision based upon a re-appraisal of interest or staff availability will result in the tender going either to an A or D category.

If the decision is D the documents are given to the Area Estimator and the procedures continue on Page T/22.

If alternatively the decision is to upgrade the tender to A then the procedures continue on Page T/16 until you reach 'Go to A'. This directs you back to Page T/8 (following the decision point - Review Category) where the Category A procedures then take you through to the end of the Tender Stage - Page T/12.

Had the tender been a Traditional Category C, A or D or a Design and Build type alternative routes are also given.

Notes for Page T/4

❏ Form QA/A Enquiry Report

The form is required to be completed in stages.

Clerical Assistant (2) completes as much as possible of the first two sections. Information for the remaining sections will be provided by the Area Estimator following the Enquiry Review. The Enquiry Review identifies the method of tendering, category of tender (this category should be reviewed following the Contract Review meeting) and staff allocated. The process by which the tender proceeds is dependent upon these decisions.

Enquiry Review meeting

At this meeting an initial decision will be taken with regard to the company's input into the tender preparation. The job will be given a Category or Type and the names of staff allocated will be stated by the Area Manager. This decision may be amended in accordance with the following timescale diagram.

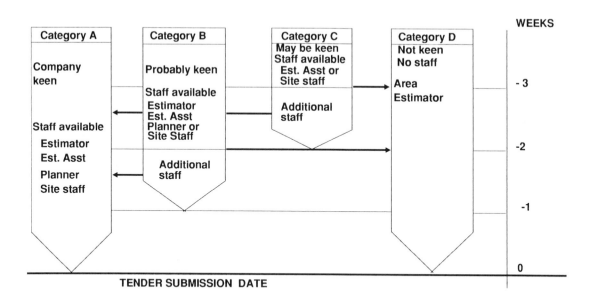

Who	Flow	Notes

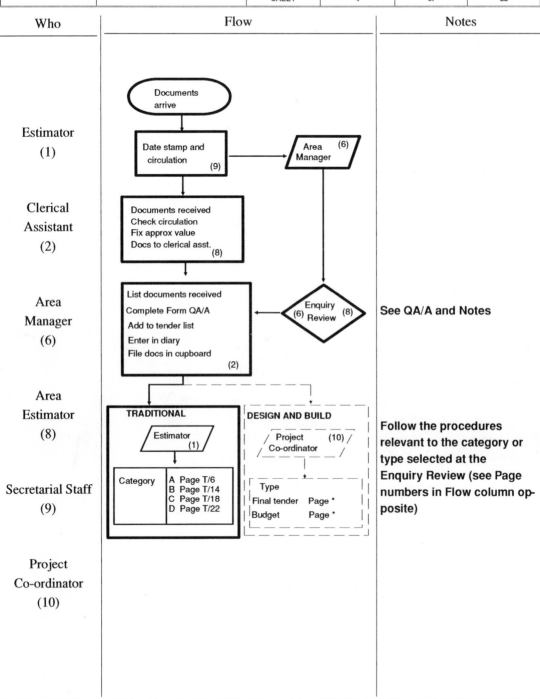

Estimator (1)

Clerical Assistant (2)

Area Manager (6)

Area Estimator (8)

Secretarial Staff (9)

Project Co-ordinator (10)

Documents arrive

Date stamp and circulation (9)

Area Manager (6)

Documents received
Check circulation
Fix approx value
Docs to clerical asst. (8)

List documents received
Complete Form QA/A
Add to tender list
Enter in diary
File docs in cupboard (2)

Enquiry (6) Review (8)

See QA/A and Notes

TRADITIONAL

Estimator (1)

Category | A Page T/6
B Page T/14
C Page T/18
D Page T/22

DESIGN AND BUILD

Project (10) Co-ordinator

Type
Final tender   Page *
Budget   Page *

Follow the procedures relevant to the category or type selected at the Enquiry Review (see Page numbers in Flow column opposite)

Notes for Page T/6   **Traditional Category A Procedure.**

❏ Form QA/A (cont'd)

The Estimator checks the form and adds any missing information. A copy of the form is to be filed in the 'Records Section' of the Main/Tender/Contract file as part of the document control procedures by the Clerical Assistant. See Document Control Procedures.

❏ Form QA/C Enquiry Procedures

The purpose of the procedures is to try and ensure that quotations used in tenders are only taken from suppliers and subcontractors that meet our Company's requirements. The form enables the Estimating Assistant/Estimator to list in abreviated form all the quotations sought from both suppliers and subcontractors and to note in the 'CAT' column the criteria by which they were included. New firms included under criterion C (or A in circumstances noted on form) must be checked by the Estimator-see Form QA/F.

Contract Review meeting and Site Visit The company needs to gain information **from** and provide information **to** the client/client's agent, on its requirements to produce a Quality Assured building. This must be done at the earliest possible stage. Details of the Agenda for this meeting will be described later under QA/G Note:- It should be made clear to the client that should this meeting not take place then the company's QA procedures cannot be fully adhered to.

❏ Form QA/D Site Visit Report

The form acts as both a checklist and permanent record of the results of a site visit. The form should be completed by the Estimator or a senior member of the site staff allocated to the project.

❏ Form QA/E Initial Review meeting

The purpose behind the meeting is to establish at an early stage:
1.   The formation of a project team.
2.   The agreement of a tender timetable.
3.   An appreciation of the adequacy of the tender information.
4.   An outline of the method and organisation envisaged.
5.   The allocation of tasks to members of the team.

The form provides a basic agenda and acts as part of a permanent record of the initial decisions taken. It also ensures that some of the questions required for the Contract Review meeting with the client are established at an early date.

❏ Form QA/F Checking Procedures

The form outlines the criteria by which the Estimator can establish a supplier's or subcontractor's conformance. Any divergence from the points listed or new criteria created should be noted. The Estimator should indicate within the 'checked' column of QA/C which of the criteria listed has enabled him to include the company. It is not required at this stage that documentary evidence of conformance be obtained.

Who	Flow	Notes

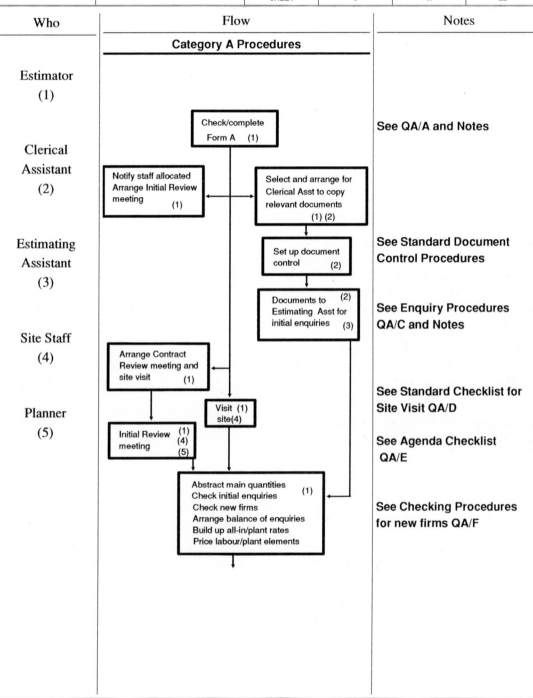

Category A Procedures

Estimator (1)

Clerical Assistant (2)

Estimating Assistant (3)

Site Staff (4)

Planner (5)

Check/complete Form A (1)

See QA/A and Notes

Notify staff allocated Arrange Initial Review meeting (1)

Select and arrange for Clerical Asst to copy relevant documents (1) (2)

Set up document control (2)

See Standard Document Control Procedures

Documents to Estimating Asst for initial enquiries (2) (3)

See Enquiry Procedures QA/C and Notes

Arrange Contract Review meeting and site visit (1)

See Standard Checklist for Site Visit QA/D

Visit (1) site(4)

Initial Review meeting (1) (4) (5)

See Agenda Checklist QA/E

Abstract main quantities Check initial enquiries Check new firms Arrange balance of enquiries Build up all-in/plant rates Price labour/plant elements (1)

See Checking Procedures for new firms QA/F

Notes for Page T/8 **Traditional Category A Procedure.**

❏ Form QA/G Contract Review

The form acts as a checklist/agenda and should be supported by brief minutes prepared by the Estimator.

Who	Flow	Notes

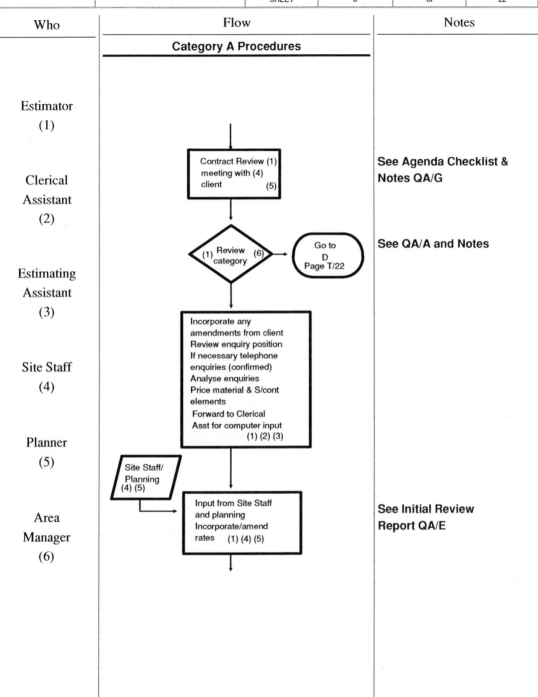

Category A Procedures

Estimator (1)

Clerical Assistant (2)

Estimating Assistant (3)

Site Staff (4)

Planner (5)

Area Manager (6)

Contract Review (1) meeting with (4) client (5)

See Agenda Checklist & Notes QA/G

(1) Review category (6) → Go to D Page T/22

See QA/A and Notes

Incorporate any amendments from client
Review enquiry position
If necessary telephone enquiries (confirmed)
Analyse enquiries
Price material & S/cont elements
Forward to Clerical Asst for computer input (1) (2) (3)

Site Staff/ Planning (4) (5)

Input from Site Staff and planning
Incorporate/amend rates (1) (4) (5)

See Initial Review Report QA/E

Notes for Page T/10   Traditional Category A Procedure.

❏ Form QA/B1 Programme and Method Review Report

The meeting should allow the Estimator to take account of the work of the Site Staff and Planner and provide a check of major elements of his tender. The form again acts as a checklist and records their discussion as an aid to the Area Manager prior to the Tender Review meeting.

❏ Form QA/B2 Estimators Report

A second estimator is required to carry out a superficial analysis of the priced BQ and will note any high or low rates in the first column. If 'own rate' what part of the rate is high or low is noted in column 2 and a brief comment made in column 4. The Estimator receives the report back from the second estimator and notes in the final column whether the tender has been amended. As with Form QA/B1 the information is provided as an aid to the Area Manager in the Tender Review meeting. It will also allow the discovery of any obvious errors that might otherwise be missed.

❏ Form QA/H Tender Review Record

The form provides an outline agenda and record of decisions taken at the Tender Review meeting.

Who	Flow	Notes

Category A Procedures

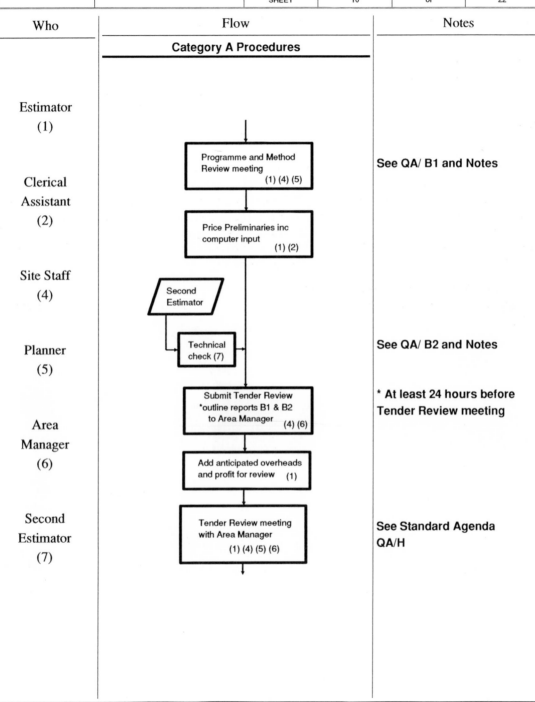

Estimator (1)

Clerical Assistant (2)

Site Staff (4)

Planner (5)

Area Manager (6)

Second Estimator (7)

Programme and Method Review meeting (1) (4) (5)

Price Preliminaries inc computer input (1) (2)

Second Estimator

Technical check (7)

Submit Tender Review *outline reports B1 & B2 to Area Manager (4) (6)

Add anticipated overheads and profit for review (1)

Tender Review meeting with Area Manager (1) (4) (5) (6)

See QA/ B1 and Notes

See QA/ B2 and Notes

* At least 24 hours before Tender Review meeting

See Standard Agenda QA/H

Notes for Page T/12   **Traditional Category A Procedure.**

There are no notes for this page.

Who	Flow	Notes

Category A Procedures

Estimator
(1)

Estimating
Assistant
(3)

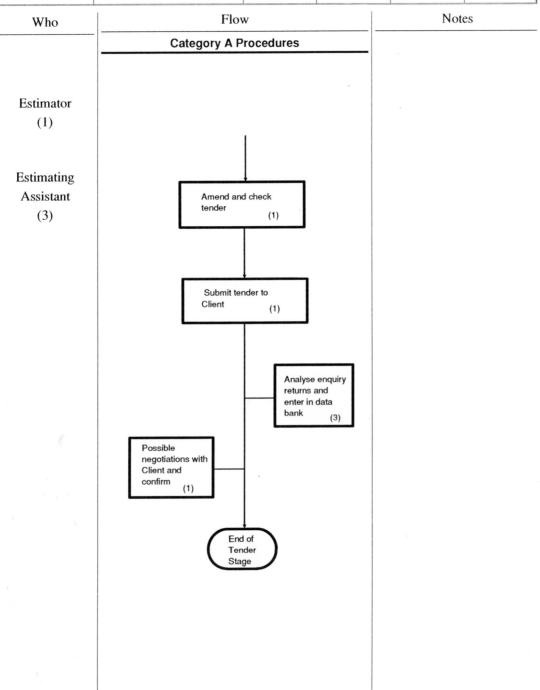

Amend and check tender (1)

Submit tender to Client (1)

Analyse enquiry returns and enter in data bank (3)

Possible negotiations with Client and confirm (1)

End of Tender Stage

Notes for Page T/14   Traditional Category B Procedure.

❏ Form QA/A (cont'd)

The Estimator checks the form and adds any missing information. A copy of the form is to be filed in the 'Records Section' of the Main/Tender/Contract file as part of the document control procedures by the Clerical Assistant. See Document Control Procedures.

❏ Form QA/C Enquiry Procedures

The purpose of the procedures is to try and ensure that quotations used in tenders are only taken from suppliers and subcontractors that meet our Company's requirements. The form enables the Estimating Assistant/Estimator to list in abbreviated form all the quotations sought from both suppliers and subcontractors and to note in the 'CAT' column the criteria by which they were included. New firms included under criterion C (or A in circumstances noted on form must be checked by the Estimator-see Form QA/F).

Contract Review meeting and Site Visit The company needs to gain information **from** and provide information **to** the client/client's agent, on its requirements to produce a Quality Assured building. This must be done at the earliest possible stage. Details of the Agenda for this meeting will be described later under QA/G. Note:- It should be made clear to the client that should this meeting not take place then the company's QA procedures cannot be fully adhered to.

❏ Form QA/D Site Visit Report

The form acts as both a checklist and permanent record of the results of a site visit. The form should be completed by the Estimator or a senior member of the site staff allocated to the project.

❏ Form QA/E Initial Review meeting

The purpose behind the meeting is to establish at an early stage:
1. The formation of a project team.
2. The agreement of a tender timetable.
3. An appreciation of the adequacy of the tender information.
4. An outline of the method and organisation envisaged.
5. The allocation of tasks to members of the team.

The form provides a basic agenda and acts as part of a permanent record of the initial decisions taken. It also ensures that some of the questions required for the Contract Review meeting with the client are established at an early date.

❏ Form QA/F Checking Procedures

The form outlines the criteria by which the Estimator can establish a suppliers' or subcontractors' conformance. Any divergence from the points listed or new criteria created should be noted. The Estimator should indicate within the 'checked' column of QA/C which of the criteria listed has enabled him to include the company. It is not required at this stage that documentary evidence of conformance be obtained.

Who	Flow	Notes

Category B Procedures

Who column:

Estimator (1)

Clerical Assistant (2)

Estimating Assistant (3)

Site Staff (4)

Planner (5)

Flow boxes:

Check/complete Form A   (1)

Notify staff allocated Arrange Initial Review meeting   (1)

Select and arrange for Clerical Asst to copy relevant documents   (1) (2)

Set up document control   (2)

Documents to Estimating Asst for initial enquiries   (2) (3)

Arrange Contract Review meeting and site visit   (1)

Initial Review meeting   (1) (4) or (5)

Visit (1) site

Abstract main quantities
Check initial enquiries
Check new firms
Arrange balance of enquiries
Build up all-in/plant rates
Price labour/plant elements   (1)

Notes column:

See QA/ A and Notes

See Standard Document Control Procedures

See Enquiry Procedures QA /C and Notes

Site Visit QA/D

See Agenda Checklist QA/E

See Checking Procedures for new firms QA/F

Notes for Page T/16   Traditional Category B Procedure.

❑ Form QA/G Contract Review

The form acts as a checklist/agenda and should be supported by brief minutes prepared by the Estimator.

If Category A.

Second Review meeting follows the pattern of the Initial Review and is intended to:

1.   Establish the enlarged project team.
2.   Critically review the original timetable.
3.   Review the increased information available in terms of of its adequacy.
4.   Gain agreement of the larger team to the method and organisation proposals.
5.   Re-allocate tasks to the enlarged team.

Who	Flow	Notes
	Category B Procedures	

Estimator (1)

Contract Review meeting with (1) Client
(4) or (5)

See Agenda Checklist & Notes QA/G

Estimating Assistant (3)

(1) Review category (6) → Go to D Page T/22

See QA/A and Notes

Site Staff (4)

Notify additional staff allocated
Arrange second review meeting with all Site Staff , Planner and Estimating Asst.
(1)

Additional staff allocated to bring input of resources up to Category A standard

Planner (5)

Hold second review meeting
Allocate new tasks to all staff
Review notes of client meeting
Review enquiry position
(1) (3) (4) (5)

Introduce new staff to project and spread tasks previously allocated to allow them to be covered in greater depth
Extra enquiries sent out may be faxed or delivered to speed up return

Area Manager (6)

Go to A

See Category A procedures on Page T/8. Continue following procedures after Review Category decision point

Procedures increased to raise to Category A standard

Notes for Page T/18   Traditional Category C Procedure.

❏ **Form QA/A (cont'd)**

The Estimator checks the form and adds any missing information. A copy of the form is to be filed in the 'Records Section' of the Main/Tender/Contract file as part of the document control procedures by the Clerical Assistant. See Document Control Procedures.

❏ **Form QA/D Site Visit Report**

The form acts as both a checklist and permanent record of the results of a site visit. The form should be completed by the Estimator or a senior member of the site staff allocated to the project.

Who	Flow	Notes

Category C Procedures

Estimator (1)

Check/complete Form A (1)

See QA/ A and Notes

Clerical Assistant (2)

Select and arrange for Clerical Asst to copy relevant documents (1) (2)

Estimating Assistant (3)

Set up document control (2)

See Standard Document Control Procedures

Documents to (2) Estimating Asst or Site Staff for initial enquiries (3) or (4)

By Estimating Asst or Site Staff depending upon availability

Site Staff (4)

Arrange Contract Appraisal meeting Arrange site visit (optional) (1)

Enquiries to be set up only (not to be sent out at this stage)

Visit site (optional) (1)

See Standard Checklist for Site Visit QA/D

Area Manager (6)

Review (1) category (6)

Go to D Page T/22

See QA/A and Notes

Notify extra staff allocated Arrange Initial Review meeting (1)

Additional staff allocated to bring input of resources up to Category A standard

Procedures increased to raise to Category A standard

Notes for Page T/20   **Traditional Category C Procedures.**

❏ Form QA/D Site Visit Report

The form acts as both a checklist and permanent record of the results of a site visit. The form should be completed by the Estimator or a senior member of the site staff allocated to the project.

❏ Form QA/C Enquiry Procedures

The purpose of the procedures is to try and ensure that quotations used in tenders are only taken from suppliers and subcontractors that meet our Company's requirements. The form enables the Estimating Assistant/Estimator to list in abreviated form all the quotations sought from both suppliers and subcontractors and to note in the 'CAT' column the criteria by which they were included. New firms included under criterion C (or A in circumstances noted on form) must be checked by the Estimator-see Form QA/F.

Contract Review meeting and Site Visit The company needs to gain information **from** and provide information **to** the client/client's agent, on its requirements to produce a Quality Assured building. This must be done at the earliest possible stage. Details of the Agenda for this meeting will be described later under QA/G. Note:- It should be made clear to the client that should this meeting not take place then the company's QA procedures cannot be fully adhered to.

❏ Form QA/E Initial Review meeting

The purpose behind the meeting is to establish at an early stage:
1. The formation of a project team.
2. The agreement of a tender timetable.
3. An appreciation of the adequacy of the tender information.
4. An outline of the method and organisation envisaged.
5. The allocation of tasks to members of the team.

The form provides a basic agenda and acts as part of a permanent record of the initial decisions taken. It also ensures that some of the questions required for the Contract Review meeting with the client are established at an early date.

❏ Form QA/F Checking Procedures

The form is a checklist only which outlines the means by which the Estimator can establish conformance. Any divergence from it or new criteria created should be noted. The Estimator should indicate within the 'checked' column of QA/C which of the criteria listed has enabled him to include the company. He is not required at this stage to obtain documentary evidence of conformance.

❏ Form QA/G Contract Review

The form acts as a checklist/agenda and should be supported by brief minutes prepared by the Estimator.

Who	Flow	Notes

Category C Procedures

Who	Flow	Notes
Estimator (1)	Arrange Contract Review meeting and site visit if not already done (1)	
Clerical Assistant (2)	Visit (1) site (4) — Arrange for Clerical Asst to produce extra copies of documents (2)	**See Standard Checklist for Site Visit QA/D**
	Estimating Asst to (3) send out enquiries	**Note : enquiries set up previously. Refer to QA/C**
Estimating Assistant (3)	Initial Review meeting (1) (4) (5)	**See Agenda Checklist QA/E**
Site Staff (4)	Abstract main quantities / Check initial enquiries / Check new firms / Arrange balance of enquiries / Build up all-in/plant rates / Price labour/plant elements (1)	**See Checking Procedures for new firms QA/F**
Area Manager (6)	Contract Review meeting with Client (1) (4) (5)	**See Agenda Checklist and Notes QA/G**
	Go to A	**See Category A procedures on Page T/8. Continue following procedures after Review Category decision point**
		Procedures increased to raise to Category A standard

Notes for Page T/22   Traditional Category D Procedures.

❏ Form QA/A (cont'd)

The Area Estimator checks the form and adds any missing information (e.g. Revised Category and date). A copy of the form is to be filed in the 'Records Section' of the Main/Tender/Contract file as part of the document control procedures by the Clerical Assistant. See Document Control Procedures.

Who	Flow	Notes

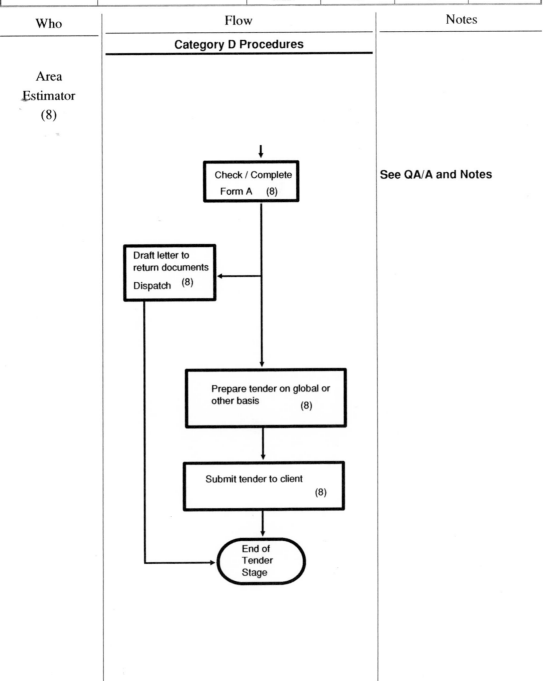

Category D Procedures

Area
Estimator
(8)

Check / Complete
Form A   (8)

Draft letter to
return documents
Dispatch   (8)

Prepare tender on global or
other basis
(8)

Submit tender to client
(8)

End of
Tender
Stage

See QA/A and Notes

This page left intentionally blank

THE SYSTEM DEVELOPED - MOBILISATION STAGE

6.0   The points addressed

The Mobilisation Stage is the period between the acceptance of a contractor's tender to the start of construction on site. This period varies considerably in length but is a vitally important timespan where available resources must be fully utilised.

As with the previous chapter the system developed for this stage addresses the same two principle issues:

- the BS requirements
- the specific problems discovered at the investigation stage.

There is of course a broadening of the relevant BS requirements by this stage although the particular clauses addressed remain as the tender stage:

4.1   Management
4.2   QA system
4.3   Contract review
4.4   Document control
4.5   Purchasing
4.8   Process control
4.15   Quality records
4.16   Audit
4.17   Training

Again the principle problems discovered at this stage and noted in the initial report occurred in the same four broad areas:

- time available for this stage could be variable but was frequently a major concern
- resources were often slow in being released from previous commitments and imbalanced in terms of skills and experience
- information tended to arrive in large and difficult to digest batches to individuals who were often unfamiliar with the project
- control was difficult in this transitional period. The site manager was often tied down with the early procurement and planning of the project. This was exacerbated by having to deal with a team and clients that were often relative strangers.

6.1 Issues considered under the relevant BS headings

6.1.1 Management

The emphasis on management here is to:

- devolve authority and responsibility
- provide resources, including information.

The early appointment of the site manager is seen as essential if the constraints of time and resources are to be minimised (diamond on Flow Chart M/2 page 81).

Staffing new projects at relatively short notice is often a compromise between the ideal and the possible.

The Pre-commencement Handover meeting establishes a formal link between the tender and production teams (Flow Chart M/2 page 81 and Agenda Form QA/L page 141). This helps ensure that the records generated in the tender stage are discussed to facilitate continuity and a rapid assimilation of key information.

The role of management falls largely to the site manager. It is important that the site manager further devolves this role, in a formal and structured way, to the initial project team. In this way whatever resources are available are used to maximum effect. (Form QA/M pages 142-143)

6.1.2 QA system

Again at this stage the system is defined, relying more on the detail contained on Forms and General Procedures than on the Flow Chart which is restricted to detailing the principal activities only.

As with the tender stage, staff and their roles are defined, albeit initially on a temporary basis. Processes are again controlled by Forms and General Procedures.

6.1.3 Contract review

Further information becomes available and has to be examined. In establishing a relationship with the client's representatives it is important to understand their intentions in terms of the provision of available and future information. This is provided by the pre-commencement meeting with the client (Flow Chart M/2 page 81 and agenda on Form QA/N page 144).

This is intended to build upon the previous pre-tender meeting, assuming it has occurred, and to provide a platform for regular meetings in the future. Early advice on the future supply of information will aid the planning and control of activities at this stage.

6.1.4 Document control

Continuity is ensured by linking the procedures applicable at this stage to those of the preceding stage. This is done by developing those procedures by increasing the sophistication of the filing system.

6.1.5 Purchasing

This is clearly more important at this stage and reference is made to Enquiry, Ordering and Quality Plan procedures all of which are designed to ensure compliance with the specified requirements. The Detailed Quality Plan will, if available, provide information of any tests or inspections which may be necessary. Orders sent to subcontractors or suppliers must provide these details and require compliance. However a general clause to require their compliance without specifically detailing the tests etc. is included within the standard enquiry form. For more detail refer to Chapter 8.

6.1.6 Process control

An early start must be made on planning and the development of any written method statements for work occurring early in the programme or with long lead-in periods.

The control of the production process is best established via the Quality Plans. Refer to Chapter 8 for a description of this procedure.

6.1.7 Quality records

Again the forms and records of meetings will provide evidence of compliance with the Quality System.

6.1.8 Audit

Compliance will largely be judged against the records provided. However it is also necessary at this stage to inspect the Quality Plans to ensure that they have been prepared in compliance with the procedures. Compliance with other General Procedures will normally be established by a planned programme of checks.

6.1.9 Training

Effective use of available staff can only be enhanced by the institution of a training programme. Whilst this programme is primarily directed towards the needs of the company it should also consider the aspirations of the individual. The procedures also provide for an accessible and comprehensive system of personnel records for management at all levels. Refer to Recruitment/Training procedures in Chapter 9.

❏ **A detailed edited extract of this section of the Manual follows.**

All pages with the QA Manual heading are taken directly from the Manual.

Notes for Page M/2   **Traditional Tender**

❏ Form QA/L Handover Meeting Record

The forms act as a checklist and record of the handover from the Tender Team to the initial Site Management team. The completed forms handed over provide basic information which together with the discussion should provide a quick insight into the project. Copies of the information to be handed over should be made available to the Site Manager at least 24 hours before the meeting. Minutes of the meeting should be taken by the Site Manager and filed together with the form in the 'Records Section' of the Project Filing System.

❏ Form QA/M Project Team Duties Review

The mobilisation period is extremely influential and should not be underrated in terms of the project's future success. The maximum amount of preparatory work possible should be undertaken during this period. The form provides a checklist and requires both a timescale to be set and the allocation of staff duties to be made at an early stage.

Refer also to - Document Control, Enquiry and Quality Plan Procedures.

The form recognises the importance of the information provided and requires its early critical examination using Form QA/V.

The early procurement of proper resources is also important to the future success of the project and should be controlled at an early stage.

❏ Form QA/ N Contract Review (Stage 2)

It is important that the company establishes good communication links at an early stage. Information has to be passed in both directions and a knowledge of the procedures of both sides helps this process.

The availability and understanding of information provided cannot commence too soon. The form again provides a checklist and can be used for brief notes. However, minutes should be taken by the company and filed, together with this form, in the Records Section of the Project Filing System.

❏ Form QA/P Pre-commencement Co-ordination Meeting

This meeting brings together the larger team now established. The duties assigned at the earlier stage are examined and reviewed in terms of progress. Duties which are incomplete may be re-allocated at this stage to involve the wider team.

A critical examination of information requirements and the quality of that provided needs to take place in order to:

1.   Allocate further duties.
2.   Decide whether an effective start is possible.

A review of the progress made in obtaining resources also takes place.

The Site Manager should make all the staff aware of their position in the team and the duties they are expected to undertake.

Who	Flow	Notes

Mobilisation Stage - Traditional Tender

Estimator
(1)

Site Staff
(4)

Planner
(5)

Area
Manager
(6)

Contracts
Manager
(12)

Site
Manager
(13)

Site
QS
(14)

Construction
Staff
(15)

All negotiation / change should be minuted or otherwise confirmed in writing

Site Manager must be appointed at this stage and is responsible for ensuring implementation of all procedures from this stage on

Site Manager to have input in selection of team

See Agenda Checklist and Notes QA/L

See QA/ M and Notes and Quality Plan Procedures

See Agenda Checklist and Notes QA/N

See Agenda Checklist and Notes QA/P

*Estimator and Planner to attend if required by Site Manager

This page left intentionally blank

THE SYSTEM DEVELOPED - CONSTRUCTION STAGE

7.0 The points addressed

By this stage the system developed had to account for all the requirements of the BS noted in Chapter 2 and further aspects of the BS requirements previously listed in Chapters 5 and 6 as follows:

4.1	Management
4.2	QA System
4.3	Contract Review
4.4	Document Control
4.5	Purchasing including Client Supplied items (4.6) and Traceability (4.7)
4.8	Process Control
4.9	Inspection and Testing including Equipment Tests (4.10), Inspection/Test status (4.11), Non-conformance Control (4.12), Corrective Action (4.13) and the use of Statistical Techniques (4.18)
4.14	Handling and Storage
4.15	Quality Records
4.16	Audit
4.17	Training

In looking at this final stage the problems are again considered in the same four areas of time, resources, information and control:

- time was found to be an increasingly common problem as construction periods on new projects were continually being squeezed. Obviously within the construction period the pressure of time was variable being linked largely to the performance and availability of resources and the consistency of information flow

- resources were extremely variable in quality and experience resulting in problems arising periodically with little or no notice preceding their occurrence

- information flow was often frequently poorly co-ordinated with production needs. The quality of information was often poor and the discovery of its shortcomings too frequently occurred after the information had been passed on for use by others

- control by management at all levels was found to be difficult. Head office management found difficulty in arriving at a balance between involvement and interference at project level. Site based management's control was often made more difficult if they were spending too much time feeding what was often regarded as superfluous information to senior management. Other problems at project level concerned the number, variety and quality of resources which the site manager was required to manage.

7.1   Issues considered under the relevant BS headings

7.1.1 Management

At this stage management is occurring both at different levels and different locations. The system must provide for senior management's role in defining, controlling and administering the system. The system is proactive in setting down the procedures that must be followed to ensure quality. It must also provide for management to be reactive in terms of developing and improving the system on the basis of the information it receives. The site manager's role is to complete the definition of the system through the production of the project specific Quality Plans. Forms and procedures are provided to aid this process, see Chapter 8.

It is recognised that the system should prevent the link between the site manager and area manager/office from becoming too impersonal and from being a one-way flow of information. The Quality Plans set down the management structure at project level, the choice of structure and individual roles. The scope and methods of control within the Quality Plan are left largely to the discretion of the site manager. The aim is to ensure that authority and responsibility for achieving quality at this level continues to rest with site management. Senior management will monitor the project's performance via Monthly Reports (Form QA/T pages 154-157) and meetings. The Quality Manager will inspect the Quality Plans and records to ensure conformance.

7.1.2 QA system

This stage defines the remainder of the system at project level through the flow chart, forms and general procedures. However the majority of the system is project specific and created by the site manager through the development of the Quality Plans. Through this the balance of roles and responsibilities are defined and the processes controlled by again using forms and procedures.

7.1.3 Contract review

The platform of regular meetings broadens to encompass particular subcontractors and suppliers to ensure that the specified requirements are understood by all parties.

7.1.4 Document control

Responsibility for ensuring the continuity of the procedures developed for the previous stage rests with the site manager.

7.1.5 Purchasing

Again Enquiry, Ordering and Quality Plan procedures apply to ensure not only compliance with specified requirements but also to stipulate that documentary evidence of compliance is to be provided where requested.Traceability i.e. records of what went where, e.g. a concrete pours record, would form part of the Quality Plans.

7.1.6 Process Control

Detailed planning and the production of written method statements or instructions should continue through the construction stage. This should be linked to the preparation of Detailed Quality Plans.

7.1.7 Inspection and Testing

The Quality Plan procedures involve the development of an Inspection and Testing Plan which combined with the Handling and Storage procedures and the check on receipt (Form QA/Y page 162) ensure that at all stages of construction compliance is verified. A record and schedule of equipment tests is incorporated in the Detailed Quality Plans, as is a system of instructions and records which enable corrective action in the event of non-conformance. The use of statistical techniques to establish statistically acceptable samples rather than blanket inspections is noted within the Quality Plan procedures. See Chapter 8.

7.1.8 Quality Records

Forms, records of meetings, and returns to head office provide evidence of compliance with the Quality System.

7.1.9 Audit

Every effort has been made with the system to avoid placing responsibility for the quality of work with the auditor (Quality Manager). What the auditor, and through the audit function management, has responsibility for, is ensuring compliance with, and or improvement of, the Quality System. The presence and authority of the auditor within the system is given a low profile. Instead, it relies heavily upon the returns to be provided by the site manager to monitor the continuing compliance with the system. This is supplemented by the auditor's wider role of support, advice and inspection described in Chapter 9.

7.1.10 Training

The Training procedures require appraisal of new and existing staff. For longer serving staff this is omitted by use of an experience waiver. Responsibility for training, identification of needs and reporting on progress is defined within these procedures. Refer to Chapter 9.

❑ **A detailed edited extract of this section of the Manual follows.**

All pages with the QA Manual heading are taken directly from the Manual.

Notes for Page C/2

❏ QA/Q Site (co-ordination) meeting timetable

The form is designed to provide the basic information required by all parties. Copies of the form providing dates for proposed meetings should be sent to participating consultants/subcontractors as soon as possible. It is recognised that subcontractors will normally attend a separate meeting. An agenda can be found on forms QA/R and QA/R(s).

❏ QA/U Information request

The form allows for written or typed requests to be submitted. You should try and ensure that your questions are sufficiently detailed and unambiguous. Two copies of the form are forwarded to the Architect who should be requested to utilise the reply section to link the response to the request. Requests should be referenced in sequence, dated and the date the information is required by entered. The persons authorised to request information will be established by their job descriptions shown in the Quality Plan - see Quality Plan Procedures.

❏ QA/V Information receipt/appraisal

It is important that all information received is recorded (see Document Control Procedures) and appraised prior to filing or forwarding onward for use by others. The aim is to ensure that the information is both correct, as best can be judged, and complete at as early a point in time as possible. This also avoids passing on unknowingly incorrect or incomplete information to those who must use it. Again duties and responsibility for appraising information will be established within the Quality Plans - see Quality Plan Procedures.

❏ QA/W

Part of the Quality Plan Procedures is to establish procedures at site level for the inspection and testing of work. The form has been designed for use as part of these procedures in inspecting our own work or our subcontractor's work. Hold points will have been defined within the Quality Plan and marked on the detailed programme. Waivers are the acceptance of work which does not conform and can only be given with the approval of the site manager.

Who	Flow	Notes

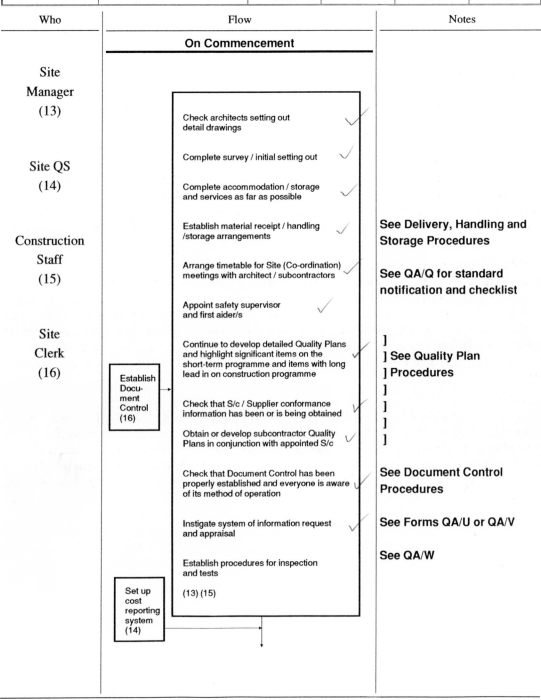

On Commencement

Site Manager (13)

Site QS (14)

Construction Staff (15)

Site Clerk (16)

Check architects setting out detail drawings

Complete survey / initial setting out

Complete accommodation / storage and services as far as possible

Establish material receipt / handling /storage arrangements

Arrange timetable for Site (Co-ordination) meetings with architect / subcontractors

Appoint safety supervisor and first aider/s

Continue to develop detailed Quality Plans and highlight significant items on the short-term programme and items with long lead in on construction programme

Check that S/c / Supplier conformance information has been or is being obtained

Obtain or develop subcontractor Quality Plans in conjunction with appointed S/c

Check that Document Control has been properly established and everyone is aware of its method of operation

Instigate system of information request and appraisal

Establish procedures for inspection and tests

Establish Document Control (16)

Set up cost reporting system (14)

(13) (15)

See Delivery, Handling and Storage Procedures

See QA/Q for standard notification and checklist

]] See Quality Plan] Procedures]]]]

See Document Control Procedures

See Forms QA/U or QA/V

See QA/W

Notes for Page C/4

❑ QA/T Monthly contract report

The report is designed, when added to others, to provide head office management with an overall picture of the company's operations. The report is to be completed in accordance with the calender issued periodically by the Area Manager. The sections of the report comprise Progress, Resources, Information and finally, and most importantly, a section for the site manager's comments. The responsibility for completing the report on time rests with the site manager. The report forms the basis of the Internal Report meeting with the Area Manager.

❑ QA/R Agenda for site construction co-ordination meetings

The purpose of these meetings is to establish a regular point of contact with the client representatives. Whilst it is probable that the Architect will have his own agenda it is important that the items listed regarding progress, information, inspection and delay are incorporated. The form is to be completed and minutes of the meeting attached when received/prepared.

❑ QA/R(s) Agenda for site subcontractors' co-ordination meetings

The purpose of the meetings is to establish a regular point of contact. It also provides a regular means of checking and recording progress and standards of work and helps to ensure a proper flow of information between the parties. Non-attendance by subcontractors should be recorded.

❑ QA/Y Material/Plant Confirmation Receipt

The form is to be used for both plant and materials although each should be listed on separate sheets. Each sheet should be referenced sequentially with the plant sheets prefixed by P and the materials sheets by M (i.e. P1, P2, M1, M2 etc.).

The sheet provides information on the receipt of materials/plant for the accounts department together with a record of its checking and comments on its condition.

❑ QA/Z Estimator feedback

In order to improve the quality of tenders the Estimator requires feedback on the performance of subcontractors, suppliers and consultants that your contract is using. In order to achieve this you are asked to enter a star rating, one to three, each month. In addition if any BQ rates are either too low or too high (remember we must be competitive) the Estimators need to know.

Who	Flow	Notes

Who

Site
Manager
(13)

Site QS
(14)

Construction
Staff
(15)

Flow

At regular intervals during construction

Maintain records of progress vis a vis programme ✓

Provide required reports to Head Office ✓

Regularly update and record information supply situation ✓

Schedule and carry out equipment tests ✓

Monitor resource value and use to date

Monitor deliveries of plant and materials and inform Accounts

Evaluate performance of S/cs, Suppliers and Consultants

Monitor and update Quality Plan and ensure inspection and test procedures are being complied with and records are being properly compiled

Hold Site (Co-ordination) meetings with Architect / Consultants

Hold Site (Co-ordination) meetings with Subcontractors including developing balance of S/c Quality Plans

Attend regular Internal Report meeting

(13)

Notes

]
]See QA/T
]

See QA/T for checklist

See Quality Plan Procedures

See QA/T

See QA/Y

See QA/Z

See Quality Plan Procedures

See QA/R for checklist agenda and notes

See QA/R(s) for checklist agenda and notes

Site Manager to discuss contents of the Contract Monthly Report with Area Manager

Notes for Page C/6

❑ QA/Z Estimator feedback

In order to improve the quality of tenders the Estimator requires feedback on the performance of subcontractors, suppliers and consultants that your contract is using. In order to achieve this you are asked to enter a star rating, one to three, each month. In addition if any BQ rates are either too low or too high (remember we must be competitive) the Estimators need to know.

Who	Flow	Notes

At regular intervals during construction

Site Manager (13)

Site QS (14)

Construction Staff (15)

Operate procedures for valuations and payments (14)

Analyse and report on variances with BQ rates (14)

Complete monthly materials reconciliation (14)

Final Account Progress Report (14)

Forward copy of Progress, Cost and Quality Test and Inspection Reports to Head Office (13)

See Valuation and Payments Procedures

See QA/Z

]
]
]
]This is to be incorporated
] within the Monthly Report
] Form QA/T by the Site
] Manager
]
]
]

On monthly or other agreed basis

Notes for Page C/8

❏ QA/Q Site (co-ordination) meeting timetable

The form is designed to provide the basic information required by all parties. Copies of the form providing dates for proposed meetings should be sent to participating consultants/subcontractors as soon as possible. It is recognised that subcontractors will normally attend a separate meeting. An agenda can be found on forms QA/R and QA/R(s).

❏ QA/X Confirmation of receipt of verbal instructions

Most building contracts provide for the formalisation of verbal instructions by the Architect by the issue of a written confirmation within a set period. The form allows designated staff (see job descriptions) to confirm such instructions promptly.

Note should also be made of any correspondence which may affect the validity of the written confirmation.

Who	Flow	Notes

On event

Site

Manager

(13)

Site QS

(14)

Construction

Staff

(15)

Place balance of subcontract/supply orders

See Enquiry Procedures

Provide new S/c with timetable for meetings

See QA/Q for standard notification and checklist

Instruct and control subcontractors

See Ordering Procedures and S/c Quality Plans

Update Quality Plans upon the receipt of significant instructions from architect

See Quality Plan

Confirm verbal instructions from Architect

See QA/X

Obtain necessary extension of time/completion certificates

(13)

Ensure that quality of records produced by others is adequate for purposes of payment / recovery (14)

Maintain necessary QS records for payment / recovery (14)

CONSTRUCTION STAGE

Notes for Page C/10

There are no notes for this page

Who	Flow	Notes

On handover

Site Manager (13)

Site QS (14)

Construction Staff (15)

Ensure necessary certificates have been issued

Obtain written list of defects

Organise the handover of maintenance manuals

Assemble complete set of quality records and forward to Client if required

Notify Head Office to contact:
*Insurers
*Bondsman
(13)

Ensure that all records required are collected and transported to Head Office and properly stored

(13)

Clear site (13) (15)

Provide information for final account / claims

Settle accounts with S/c

Agree final account/claims

Obtain Final Certificate (14)

Collate defect notifications

Co-ordinate the making good of defects

Obtain Making Good Defects Certificate (13) (14) or (*)

Finish

See Quality Plan

(*) Person responsible will be dependent upon availability. Contracts Manager must give written notification of person appointed

This page left intentionally blank

THE SYSTEM DEVELOPED - GENERAL PROCEDURES

8.0   Introduction

As was noted briefly in Chapter 4 and referred to in the Introduction and Flow Charts of Chapters 5 to 7 we have, for reasons of brevity, continuity or flexibility produced certain areas of the system in the form of General Procedures. The most important examples of these were the Document Control and Quality Plan Procedures. Our discussion of the core of the QA system therefore would not be complete without the inclusion and explanation of these examples.

8.1   Document Control Procedures

The principle is to ensure the traceability and control of all documents and their enclosures. In order to achieve this all documents are recorded upon receipt or dispatch and given a reference. In addition the circulation of the documents is also recorded so the company knows who had what and when. It was noted in the investigation that documents were both received and sent by potentially different groups of individuals at the various stages of the project so there was a need to establish continuity. It was also recognised that establishing the full document control system for all tenders was potentially wasteful of resources. Therefore at the tender stage a modified version of the procedures shown hereafter was produced, establishing continuity in its use of codes but allowing less complexity in its method of filing.

A particular problem noted in developing these procedures was to design a drawing register which allowed room for recording circulation whilst accommodating the issue of revisions and retaining a sequential listing of drawings. Although the forms illustrated are actually A3 size there will still be problems in establishing how much space to leave between items for a potentially large number of revisions. A better system, if facilities exist, would be to use computer based spread sheet versions of the forms with paper copies retained in a back-up file. The use of such a system will allow the insertion of extra lines between drawing references. The person with responsibility for ensuring that superseded drawings are not used must be established. The control of other documents is established by the Site Manager within the Quality Plans.

8.2   Quality Plan Procedures

The procedures allow the completion of the quality system in a project specific format. Responsibility for its completion has preferably to remain with those responsible for its implementation, hopefully generating thereby a sense of property. The requirements therefore have to be clearly explained but at the same time allow the site manager the maximum flexibility possible. It was recognised that initially there would probably be a need to provide guidance or even assistance in preparing the Quality Plan but the site manager must always remain responsible for the final product. The sequence of general and detailed Quality Plans recognises the reality in terms of time, resources and information flow in most project situations. A good Quality Plan needs to use the best available information and this will not always be available early in a project. This also accommodates the fact that the Quality Plan will be subject to change if significant variations occur.

The Quality Plan procedures are a key element within the Quality System. It is therefore essential that all those responsible for their preparation attend a course of instruction concerning their preparation and receive some explanation and practice in the use of the procedures described later in this chapter.

❏ **A detailed edited extract of this section of the Manual follows.**

All pages with the QA Manual heading are taken directly from the Manual.

Document Control Procedures

Generally

The object of these procedures is to increase the traceability of every significant piece of information issued during a project.

All incoming and outgoing documents should be recorded **including their enclosures.**

Mobilisation / Construction Stage

At the commencement of each project, files should be established with the following sections:

A. Head office

1. Records Section.
2. Incoming Correspondence.
3. Outgoing Correspondence.
4. Internal Correspondence.

A master copy of all documents should be kept in these files and not be removed. These should either be originals or you should ensure that photocopies contain all relevant information (eg small print on the back of quotations).

B. Site

1. Correspondence to and from Architect in separate sections. Minutes of meetings to be filed in a separate section.
2. Correspondence to and from Subcontractors in alphabetical order. Instructions to Subcontractors filed in separate sections.
3. Correspondence to and from Materials Suppliers in alphabetical order.
4. Correspondence to and from Plant Suppliers in alphabetical order.
5. Architects Instructions, Clerk of Works directions and Confirmation of Verbal Instructions in separate sections.
6. Requests for Information and replies.
7. Quotations from possible future Subcontractors and Suppliers or Plant Hirers.
8. Records (a copy of all records to be retained on site).
9. Tender make up and costing information.
10. Applications, Valuations and Certificates.
11. Internal Correspondence and Safety.

12. Contract Documents File (a single copy of **ALL** contract docs. should be kept in this file) Note - the contents are only to be listed in the Quality Plan file.
13. Quality Plan file, refer to the Quality Plan procedures for contents.
14. Master Index file.

The face of the file/files should be marked with the Contract Number, Project Name and contents in accordance with the above. Continuation files should be numbered sequentially dated from * and to *. Completed files should be marked as continued on File No. * which is the next file.

❏ Form DC1 Correspondence Index

This form is used first to create the Master Index of all correspondence received or sent. It should also be used as a standard index at the front of each of the files or sections noted previously. The brief information it contains can be used to trace particular items of correspondence either from the Master Index or the Section Index. Note the form is designed for use in recording either receipts or dispatches.

DATE	CODE	FROM/TO	ITEM REF	ITEM DATE	DESCRIPTION	ENCLOSURES	CIRCULATION
28/03/9*	S/MC/29	B.G. Supplies	Bg / 11	24/03/9*	Hardcore quote	None	Agent/file
01/04/9*	A/MC/26	A.N. Arch	An / 2	28/03/9*	Instruction	See DC4	Agent/QS/file
01/04/9*	Sc/MC/44	Robins & Dark	Rd/ 10	27/03/9*	Steelwork info	See DC4	Agent/Arch/file

The majority of columns to be completed are self explanatory. The code column is incorporated to enable easy reference as to the nature of the item of correspondence described.

Examples of codes to be used are as follows:

MC/A   . . Letter to Architect/Engineer
A/MC   . . Letter from Architect/Engineer
MC/Sc . . Letter to Sub-contractor
Sc/MC . . Letter from Sub-contractor
MC/S   . . Letter to Supplier (inc Plant Hirers)

S/MC . . Letter from Supplier (inc Plant Hirers)
M . . . . Minutes of Meeting with Architect/Engineer
AI . . . . Architect's Instruction
SI . . . . Clerk of Work's Direction/Site Instruction
Q . . . . . Quotation from possible future S/c / Supplier/ Plant Hirer
I . . . . . Invoice from Supplier
S . . . . . Statement of Account
RRI . . Reply to Request for Information
IM . . . . Internal Memo
RI . . . . Request for Information
CRI . . Confirmation of Receipt of Verbal Instructions
ISC . . Instruction to Sub-contractor
O . . . . . Order for materials/plant
T . . . . . Termination of hire note
SF . . . . Standard Forms followed by their reference letter e.g. SFQA/A etc.

An explanation of any non-standard codes should be attached to the Master Index.

An example of the code therefore could be:

A / MC /26

- **A / MC** means an Architect's letter sent to the Main Contractor

- **/ 26** indicates that it is letter number 26 of this code

Where form DC1 requires the Item Ref and Item Date above, it requires the reference and date shown on the letter referred to, whereas the first date column is the date the letter was received by the company.

The Records file should contain on conclusion of the construction stage all completed forms noted during the appropriate flow chart procedures plus all tests and inspections detailed in the Quality Plan. A copy of all documents issued should be kept in the Contract Documents file.

If correspondence has a number of enclosures also use Form DC4.

❏ Form DC4 Enclosures Record

Enclosures should always be fully documented. Whenever it is necessary to document enclosures this form should be used and referenced back to the main information shown on DC1.

DATE	CODE	FROM / TO	ENCLOSURES
01 / 04 / 9*	A/MC/26	A.N. Architecture	Drawings 2056/101A, 107C, 112D, 115 F and
			2055/45C
01 / 04 / 9*	Sc/MC/44	Robins and Dark Ltd	Fabrication drwgs 01/1 - 01/10 and Spec pages 1 - 8

Give the full reference of the enclosures in the above **Enclosures** column and use more than one line if necessary. If we look at example A/MC/26 you see on DC1 that this is an instruction with enclosures. For the enclosures on DC4 you would then look for the appropriate date and then the correct code.

Drawing Register

A Drawing Register must be established using Forms DC2 and DC3.

❏ DC2 Master Register

Enables you to establish standard circulation lists for drawings. All individuals or companies to be issued with information are given a number on the Master Circulation List and the number of copies they receive is entered in the right hand column. This portion of the form is completed independently from the Drawing Schedule. When the Drawing Schedule itself is filled in the form is used as a master index for the various sources or series of drawings. These drawings from different sources, series or titles can each be given up to three standard circulation lists as example below:

SOURCE	SERIES NUMBER	TITLE	STANDARD CIRCULATION												KEY MASTER CIRCULATION LIST		No Cop
			A				B				C						
A. Arch	100	Plans	1	2	3	4	1	2	4	5	3	4	5	6	1	Site	5
			8	9	10	15					10	11	12		2	Evans Flooring	1
															3	Jones Tiles	1
A.Arch	100	Elev-ations	1	5	6	7									4	Whyte Plumbing	1
															5	Smith Windows	1
															6	Acme Cladding	1
															7	Tog Painting	1

In the example the Architect's plans and elevations are treated as different titles which will have different circulation lists. In addition each drawing received should be entered on Form DC3.

❑ DC3 Detailed Register

Drawings from different sources or a different series should be entered on separate sheets and each sheet should be numbered consecutively to form a complete register. The Drawing number, title, revision letter and the date of issue should be entered. Circulation can either be a standard circulation list (see DC2) or numbers drawn from the Master Index on DC2. With each revision this circulation can be amended.

DRAWING NUMBER	TITLE	REVISION PREFIX / DATE AND CIRCULATION					
		REV	CIRC.	REV	CIRC	REV	CIRC.
		DATE		DATE		DATE	
100 / 10	Ground floor plan	A	A	B	B		
		08-06-9*		23-07-9*			
100 / 11	First floor plan	A	A	B	B	C	1, 2, 3, 6
		08-06-9*		30-07-9*		14-08-9*	

On the conclusion of the contract the above forms will provide a record of all the drawings received and to whom each and every issue has been circulated.

Note - the person entering revisions on the Drawing Register is responsible for ensuring that the retained copies of the preceding issue are marked superseded and that those circulated with copies of the previous drawing are notified.

Quality Plan Procedures

Generally

The Quality Plan is drawn up to help the site manager firstly define and subsequently control the quality requirements of the project. Its production requires analysis of the work and the abstraction of imposed quality requirements from the project documentation. In addition the project management team must establish and define their own (and the company's) requirements for the inspection and control of quality.

The Quality Plan is formulated in two stages:

- the general overall plan called the General Plan and
- detailed Plans which follow the broad outline on the General Plan.

The General Plan shall be prepared prior to the commencement of building operations. On completion of the General Plan a copy shall be forwarded to the Quality Assurance Manager.

The site manager is responsible for the Quality Plan though its preparation may be delegated. The site manager or member of the site staff shall be **named** as responsible for the implementation and monitoring of the Quality Plan.

If you examine the first flow chart, GP/QP2, this indicates the initial processes involved in setting up the Quality Plan. The why, the what, the when and where, the who and the how are explained as follows:

The why may be our own aims, local authority or client requirements.

The what requires that questions are asked. For example is it a key element, does the work require close control, does the specification require inspections or tests etc?

The when and where will be identifiable from the programmes and thus these must be prepared prior to, or in conjunction with, the Quality Plan.

Who does it The site manager is always responsible for the Quality Plan but may delegate another to produce it.
Note the input that may be required from subcontractors.

How it is to be tested or inspected may be dictated by a number of sources; examples of these are listed on the flow chart.

All of the above are brought together in the Quality Plan.

THE REASONS FOR SETTING UP THE QUALITY PLAN

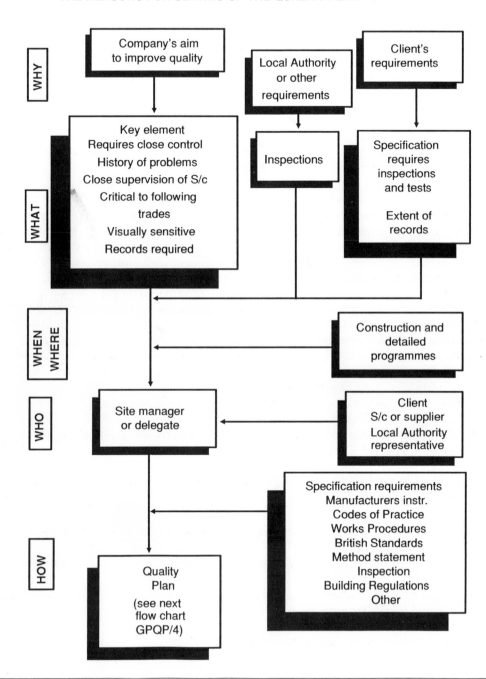

The Quality Plan

The Quality Plan is first prepared in general terms. Detailed Plans are then prepared, in sections, with the first priority given to the early operations or operations with a long lead-in. The detailed sub-programmes for these early operations must be prepared to enable a clear examination of the precise work involved.

Refer now to the flowchart GPQP/4 on the next page.

As you will note the first task is to draft a complete schedule of the drawings, specifications and other documents from which the Plan is prepared.

This schedule of documents, together with your own requirements and any subcontractors' plans which may be available, form the data source from which the plan is prepared. The contract programme then tells you when and where and enables the completion of the General Quality Plan using form QP1. In addition any necessary or available sections of the Detailed Quality Plan can be completed using form QP2 supported by the Test and Inspection Plan Form QP3.

Having prepared the Quality Plan, items such as hold points should then be marked on the construction programme. This acts as a visual aid in monitoring their compliance relative to progress. This process should, if possible, be completed during the mobilisation/pre-construction period. However it is accepted that it may also span the construction period itself. In addition it is almost certain that further Detailed Quality Plans or amended Quality Plans will be prepared at intervals during construction.

The forms, QP1-3, are designed to relate to the operations (by name, number or both) shown on the construction programme or sub-operations shown on detailed sub-programmes.

Look first at the General Quality Plan on the next but one page reference GPQP/5.

SETTING UP THE QUALITY PLAN

MOBILISATION / PRE-CONSTRUCTION

Schedule of Documents

Detailed Sub-programmes if available

Company/Site managers quality req'ts

Subcontractors' Quality Plans if available

Study of documents/ Quality requirements operation by operation to complete General Quality Plan Form QP1 plus any Detailed Quality Plans on QP2

Copy to QA Manager

Establish Inspection/Test requirements and form of records Form QP3

Mark up on programme quality requirements

AT INTERVALS DURING CONSTRUCTION

Subcontractors' Quality Plans

See decision chart overleaf

Further detailed sub-programmes

Updated information

Copy to QA Manager

Revise / extend Quality Plans
Revise / extend Inspection/Test req'ts
Revise programme if necessary
Mark up new quality requirements

❑ QP/1 General Quality Plan

QA MANUAL	General quality plan	SECTION	Company Procedures		
		STAGE	General		
		REF	QAM 4.2.4	QP1	
		REV		DATE	
		SHEET		of	

Project name			Ref		Date	
Operation/ sub-op	Detailed QP ref	Spec. reqm'ts	Client/3rd p approval	MC control type	S/c QP reqd	Other
10 Substructure						
13 Hardcore	Sheet 4	BQ Preambles	Yes	Certificate	-	-

Operation/sub-op - allows you to list the operations as known at that stage in sequence allowing space for additional operations if they are thought likely.

Detailed QP ref - makes provision to cross reference to the Detailed Quality Plan when prepared.

Spec. reqm'ts - allows you to note in general terms the source of the control requirements.

Client/3rd p approval - allows a simple yes or no in terms of whether the control requirements also involve client or another third party's approval.

MC control type - i.e. a test, an inspection, a certificate, a method statement etc.

S/c QP reqd. - recognises the input which may be necessary from subcontractors in certain operations or sub-operations.

Other - allows space for any other points you may consider relevant.

Having worked through all the known operations and utilised the general information available it is then necessary for you to consider the availability of information for sections of the Detailed Quality Plan.

❏ QP/2 Detailed Quality Plans

These are generally formulated from detailed sub-programmes but may obviously be taken from the construction programme if it is sufficiently detailed. Individual sections of the Detailed Quality Plan **must** be completed before the work they are related to is constructed, and immediately forwarded, together with any amendments to the General Quality Plan, to the Quality Manager.

		SECTION		Company Procedures	
QA		STAGE		General	
MANUAL	Detailed Quality Plan	REF	QAM 4.2.4	QP2	
		REV		DATE	
		SHEET		of	

Project name				Ref			Date		
Operation/	Spec reqm'ts		MC reqm'ts	S/c/ Sup/MC	Test /Ins	Hold point	Client/3rd p	Other	
sub-op	Doc ref	Code	code	QP ref	ref	ref	approval	reqm'ts
10 Substructures								
13 Hardcore	BQ 2/56C	C2	-	-	Sheet 2	13/1	Yes	-

Form QP2, the Detailed Quality Plan, should follow the general plan in terms of format but may obviously expand the number of operations or sub-operations. Once sub-operations have been added on the Detailed Quality Plan they should also be referenced within an amended section of the General Quality Plan. This second form allows more room for detail.

Operation/sub-op - has the same function as on the Form QP/1 - to identify by name or number the operation.

Spec reqm'ts - this column requires **precise** information rather than the general information on QP1: firstly of the document reference from which the specification requirement comes; secondly to identify the nature of that requirement in the form of a code e.g. T1 - test type 1, C1 - certificate type 1 etc.

Note - a key to these codes must be included with the plan.

MC reqm'ts - indicates that the imposed quality requirement is our own and should be entered using a similar system of codes. These will include references to method

---

statements and works procedures which can be developed from the guidance notes for works procedures. Examples attached are Sheets SD/WP/30 and SD/WP/14.

SD/WG/30 refers to drainage runs listing typical activities to be considered and the general points at which control by the use of a hold point could be established. These are of course general lists of both activities and hold points and must be applied repeatedly to the individual lengths of drain runs present to build up a total picture of this section of the Detailed Quality Plan.

Similarly other works procedures such as SD/WP/14 Brick/Blockwork (General) lists activities and hold points and may, in their case, be divided into grid references around and within the building.

S/c/Sup/MC QP ref - a significant number of operations are likely to be sublet so it may be necessary to prepare with, or obtain from, a subcontractor or supplier a section of the Quality Plan. This is discussed in more detail later but suffice it to say at this point that you cross reference your Quality Plan here to any subcontractor or supplier Quality Plan.

Test/Ins ref - allows you to enter a cross reference to the Test and Inspection Plan which expands the detail of this section on Form QP3 which will be considered shortly.

Hold point ref - allow you to establish inspection points within the construction. They operate using Form QA/Y in preventing progress without approval. They are designed for use by subcontractors and our own labour. Hold points are identified by the operation number and sequentially i.e. 23/10 would be the 10th hold point for operation No. 23.

Client/3rd p approval - allows you to note any client or third party approval normally as a Yes or No against the more detailed list of preceding items.

Other reqm'ts - again allows space for points considered relevant.

The final form for use in this process is the Test and Inspection Plan QP/3.

❏ QP/3 Test/Inspection Plan

		SECTION	Company Procedures	
QA MANUAL	Test / Inspection Plan	STAGE	General	
		REF	QAM 4.2.4	QP3
		REV		DATE
		SHEET		of

Project name			Ref	Date		
Operation	Test / inspect		Staff	Records		
sub-op	Type	When	responsible	Type	To	Stored
10 Substructures						
13 Hardcore	Sulphate content	Before	Site manager	Certificate	Client/Site	Site/head office
		commencement			head office	

Operation/sub-op - again the form starts with the operation name or number.

Test/inspect - gives details of the test or inspection required:

- the description of the type of test
- when and where it will occur i.e. daily, at the end of the operation etc.

Staff responsible - names the person responsible for:

- ensuring that the requirement is properly executed
- providing the appropriate records.

Note - this person could be external to the organisation if no other option is possible.

Records - establishes:

- the type of records e.g. completed form, certificate, marked up drawing etc.
- where the records go e.g. copy in site file, copy to Head Office
- where they are stored.

Subcontractors and suppliers

As was noted in completing the forms a substantial proportion of work is likely to be sublet so it may be necessary to cover these sublet elements with the subcontractors' own Quality Plans. The final diagram GPQP/10 is a decision chart which assists you in deciding the route to be taken in obtaining a Quality Plan from a subcontractor.

Looking at the diagram GPQP/10 the first decision is whether your subcontractor or supplier actually needs their own separate plan.

If **NO** you inspect and approve their work yourself within your own test and inspection plan. If **YES** you must first discover whether the subcontractor or supplier operates their own QA System in accordance with BS 5750. This information is available on Record Form QA/F. If they do have their own QA System you request them to submit their Quality Plan for approval. If **NO** you should enquire with the subcontractor whether they require to use our standard planning forms QP/2 and 3. If **NO**, again they prepare it in their own format in accordance with the principles set out in Section 7 of the Quality Plan file noted on GPQP/14 hereafter.

Note - the points listed in that section numbered 1 to 10 form part of the standard enquiry conditions and are also incorporated in their subcontract conditions. If it is **YES** to using our standard forms copies are provided with a note that column 5 is to be left blank; we will then use this to cross reference to our own Quality Plans.

It must be recognised, at this stage, that in addition to setting out the imposed quality requirements within their subcontract, we must also be prepared to offer some guidance to certain subcontractors in their preparation of their Quality Plans.

The final stages are to check that the particular requirements notified within the enquiry and subcontract documents and listed in Section 7 hereafter are incorporated in their Quality Plan; finally to inspect and to approve the subcontractors/suppliers work at the hold points established with them and noted within their agreed Quality Plans.

SECTION	Company Procedures		
STAGE	General		
REF	QAM 4.2.4	GPQP/10	
REV		DATE	
SHEET	10	of	14

QA MANUAL — Quality Plan Procedures

DECISION CHART FOR PREPARATION OF DETAILED QUALITY PLANS FOR SUBCONTRACTORS/SUPPLIERS

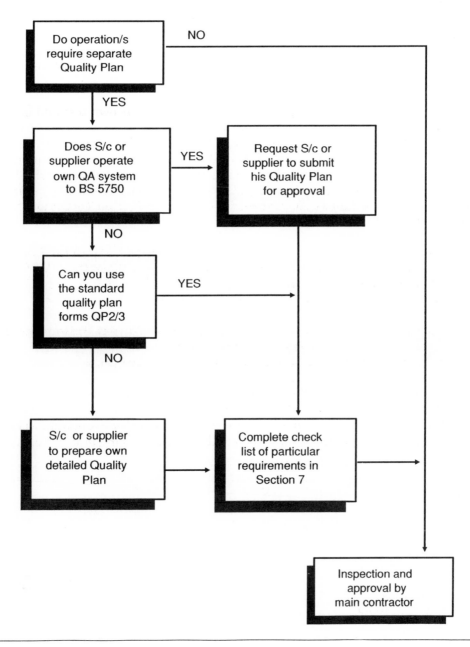

The contents of the Quality Plan file

The Quality Plan for each project shall be held in its own file divided into the following sections:

1. Project particulars (based upon Form QA/A and updated).
2. Schedule of contract documents - checked monthly or at shorter intervals to be specified by the site manager.
3. Site organisational structure and procedures - initial and updated.
4. Contract programme and detailed sub-programmes.
5. General Quality Plan - initial and updated.
6. Detailed Quality Plans.
7. Subcontractors' detailed Quality Plans.

Amplification of Quality Plan section contents

1. Project particulars

This section is based on checking and updating Form QA/A and should include the names and addresses of the principal parties to the contract and the design team. It should in particular state their representatives having responsibility for quality.

2. Schedule of contract documents

This will **list** the documents comprising the contract, typically the Employer's bills of quantities, specification(s), drawings and any related correspondence.

3. Site organisational structure and procedures

This is to comprise the following.

3.1 Charts
1. Area management structure chart showing lines of responsibility from site manager up to area manager including any off-site services.
2. The client and design teams' organisational structure as related to the project in as much detail as possible.
3. A site management structure chart showing job functions and lines of responsibility. This should include all staff having a supervisory or administrative role.

3.2 Schedules
1. Showing names, addresses and telephone numbers for each person shown on the charts.
2. Giving job descriptions. The duties of all administrative or supervisory staff where at variance with the standard job descriptions. See also Form QA/P and update.

3. Showing subcontractors and suppliers names, addresses, telephone numbers and personal contacts.
4. Showing the programme of formal meetings with the client / subcontractors as Form QA/Q and updates.

3.3 Written procedures

1. For communicating instructions, variations and information to the point of work.
2. For distribution and registration of drawings (also see Document Control Procedures).
3. For recording of telephone conversations, verbal instructions (see QA/X), informal meetings.
4. For obtaining third party approvals.

4. Contract programme and detailed sub-programmes

This section incorporates a copy of the latest and all previous contract programmes clearly marked as superseded. Also included are procedures for the monitoring and review of the current programme.

Procedures must be included for the preparation of detailed and sectional programmes, weekly work plans etc. Information must be included to indicate dates for receipt of design information and placing of orders, allowing a suitable time period for inspection of information.

Note - Form QA/V should be used taking the document control reference shown on DC1 and 2 and allowing a record to be kept of its appraisal.

5. General Quality Plans

Each operation on the construction programme should be examined and a plan drawn up for its effective control.

The complexity of the plan will be dependent upon the amount of information available, at this early stage, the type of work and whether it will remain available for inspection. Other factors to consider for this initial plan are:

- does the specification call for inspections and tests
- is it a key element; does it require close quality control
- is there a history of past failures or problems
- how critical is it to following trades
- will it be difficult to gain access to later

- does the subcontractor carrying out the work require careful supervision.

6. Detailed quality plans

As the contract progresses, more information becomes available or variations are issued and the general plan can be expanded and updated. Detailed Quality Plans must be prepared prior to the commencement of each operation and a copy of both detailed and revised General Plan must immediately be forwarded to the QA Manager.

A Detailed Quality Plan will consider:

1. Preparation and review of detailed programme.
2. Specific requirements for work guidance notes.
3. Specific requirements for design and materials approvals.
4. Records to be completed and returned to the main contractor.
5. Use of check sheets and requests for inspection. (See Form QA/W)
6. Inspection and test requirements.
7. Can we use statistical techniques to establish test/inspection requirements. Identification of the subcontractors' person-in-charge of site operations.
8. Any samples or mock-ups required.
9. Requirements for commissioning and provision of as-built drawings and/or maintenance manuals.
10. Quality Plans required to be prepared by subcontractors.

It is also necessary to accommodate work by subcontractors by incorporating their Quality Plans.

7. Subcontractor Quality Plan

This plan applies to those subcontractors or suppliers who do not have a BS 5750 Quality System approved by an accrediting body. Those that do will submit for approval their own Quality Plan.

Subcontractors who do not have their own Quality System should submit a Quality Plan in accordance with the following points (as required by their subcontract agreement):

1. A programme of subcontract works shall be drawn up by the subcontractor and agreed with the main contractor. It shall show the dates for receipt and approval of the supplier's drawings, information, etc. where required under the subcontract.
2. A comprehensive schedule of inspections and tests shall be prepared by the subcontractor. Acceptance standards shall be ascertained by reference to the specification.
3. The above must be approved in writing by the site manager before work commences.
4. The subcontractor must name the person based upon the site who will be responsible for quality.
5. The points of inspection of work by the main contractor must be noted on the Quality Plan. The work where covered should be scheduled for inspection and approved before it is concealed.
6. Records shall be maintained by the subcontractor and submitted to the main contractor detailing:

    *   conformance of materials to specification

    *   inspection and test certificates

    *   as-built documentation

    *   operating and maintenance manuals.

7. The subcontractor is to use the contractor's work procedures when requested by the site manager.
8. All work must conform with the specification for work to proceed beyond a specified hold point. Only non-conformances covered by a Waiver will be accepted into the works. Such acceptance or waivers will be confirmed in writing by the main contractor's specified representative(s) using Form QA/W.
9. Any approvals given on Form QA/W are made with the objective of progressing the work. However, the subcontractor should note that all work is subject to final inspection and client approval at date of handover of the works.

		SECTION		Supporting Documentation	
		STAGE		Mobilisation / Construction	
		REF	QAM 5.2	SD/WP/30	
		REV		DATE	
		SHEET	1	of	1

Activity \ Inspection / Hold point	Pre-commencement	Before starting excavation	Before laying bedding	Before laying pipes and regularly during laying	Before placing concrete, surround or backfill	Periodically during back-fill operation	Before completion	
Materials : Compliance with spec. Certificate	●							
Setting out control: Line / Level		●						
Permit to dig: Service clearance obtained		●						
Information to gang: O/s to C.L. depth to invert and exc. Pipe type, size. Branches type, depth bedding surround		●						
Excavation: Suitability, width, depth of trench, formation, support			●					
Bedding: Depth, material				●				
Pipe laying, jointing: Depth of bed, line, level, invert supported, correct type, dia. of pipe, number and size of branches				●	●			
Initial test: Type					●			
Surround: Compaction, pipe, line/level OK? Branches closed off and location recorded						●		
Backfilling: Compaction? Material?						●		
Final test: Type, flushing and proving of lines and branches							●	

QA MANUAL	Brick/blockwork (General)		

SECTION		Supporting Documentation	
STAGE		Mobilisation / Construction	
REF	QAM 5.2	SD/WP/14	
REV		DATE	
SHEET	1	of	1

Activity \ Inspection/ Hold point	Pre-commencement	Test panel	Post commencement - daily	Up to DPC	Every 1.2m vertically	At cill, head, jambs of all openings	Before closing all cavities	At installation of cloaks, trays, flashings	Before striking scaffolding
Materials: Compliance with spec. Certificate	●								
Setting out: Dimension check Line/level/plumb Position of openings, features etc.	●			●		●			
Building tolerances: Bricks, overall, openings	●								
Appearance: Brick, mortar, joint width, pointing *(Cleanliness, uniform colour, texture etc).*		●	●		●				●
Mortar mix: Batch controls?			●						
Beds and Perps: Filled?			●	●	●		●		
Ties: Number/spacing, type, cleanliness, slope/drip, position *(General/corners/openings)*			●		●	●	●		
Insulation: Cut/fixed correctly Cavity gap			●		●		●		
Cavity: Width, clean, boards/battens in use, sand beds for cleaning			●	●	●		●		
Dpc/trays/flashings: Position, fixing, continuity joints, correct type/detail				●		●	●	●	
Weepholes: Position, number, clear?						●	●		●

This page intentionally left blank

THE SYSTEM DEVELOPED - OTHER ISSUES

9.0 General

Having examined most elements of the system developed we need also to consider some other issues which have been briefly referred to but not detailed within areas of the system discussed. These issues are:

1. Audit, records and feedback.
2. The Quality Manager.
3. Recruitment, Education and Training.
4. Familiarisation.

9.1 Audit, records and feedback

A detailed guide to Quality Systems Auditing can be found in BS 7229 : 1989 which specifies objectives, responsibilities, roles and audit procedures. This BS is suitable for both internal and external audits.

BS 5750 : Part 4 : 1990 provides a definition of internal audits, under Clause 4.16, which states that such audits are designed to ensure:

- that the quality system documentation adequately defines the needs of the business

- that the documented procedures are practical, understood and followed

- that the training is adequate.

Essentially the internal audit checks the system, whether it is comprehensive enough, whether the procedures work and whether they are being used. The training aspect ensures that those involved in operating the system and producing the work are adequately qualified to do so. Training will be examined later in this chapter.

As was stated in Chapter 2, BS 5750 requires that the system should define a planned sequence of internal audits. It is however recognised that certain elements within the system are more important than others and should be given more frequent attention. The emphasis given within these procedures was that:

1. An examination and checklist be completed for all Quality Plans and amended plans within two weeks of their submission by the site manager.

2. A monthly check of head office files be undertaken to ensure that the appropriate forms relative to the stage of progress have been adequately completed. This check would cover a third of all current projects, all of which would then be covered over a three month period.

3. An initial visit be made to all projects within their first three months to check the adequacy of the Quality Plan vis a vis:

- contract documentation

- progress.

During this visit checks would also be made of the site's Quality Plan file (see Written procedures Chapter 8 Section 3.3 Page 115) and Document Control procedures.

Within the system this initial visit is described as a guidance session which results in the preparation with the site manager of a joint report forwarded to the area manager.

Details of these checks together with other less frequent checks and a notice of corrective action would then form the basis of a monthly quality report from the Quality Manager to the area manager.

The system also defines through its Audit procedures that new audit programmes are to be agreed and recorded with the area manager every three months. These programmes can also vary the frequency of checks set out in the Audit procedures (not detailed in this book).

BS 5750 requires that results of the audits must be documented and note the following:

- the deficiencies found

- the corrective action required

- the time agreed for corrective action to be carried out

- the person responsible for carrying out the corrective action.

The audit of the system will probably reveal deficiencies within the system and require corrective action. The responsibility for corrective action with respect to the system, is placed with the Quality Manager. Responsibility for corrective action due to non-use of the system is placed elsewhere (estimator, site manager etc.) but authority to instruct the correction of the deficiency is again placed with the Quality Manager. It is recognised that with such authority vested in the Quality Manager, its application should be exercised with care to avoid alienating those responsible for using the system.

A further requirement of the British Standard is that the person or persons conducting the audit should be properly trained. This can be achieved through courses which are organised by third party certifiers and consultants.

9.2 The Quality Manager

9.2.1 Why

The necessity for such an individual stems from BS 5750 : Part 2 : 1990 Clause 4.1 that requires management to appoint or nominate a management representative with defined authority and responsibility for ensuring that the requirements of the Quality System are implemented and maintained. The planned sequence of internal audits are part of that maintenance function and logically require that the management appointee or nominee should be responsible for them. Furthermore the audit Clause 4.16 requires that the auditor should be independent of the project structure and report directly to senior management. It therefore appears to be an extension of this logic that the functions of the Quality Manager should be:

- ensuring compliance and maintenance of the system
- responsibility for planning and implementing audits
- overseeing the adequacy of the company's training
- familiarising staff with the concept and use of the QA system.

9.2.2 Who

Bearing in mind these functions what sort of person should a company be looking for.

There may be a tendency to look for someone with a depth of knowledge and expertise in the technical or practical area of construction. A closer examination of the role of the individual seems to indicate that the skills required are primarily communicative and organisational. Within the particular system that we have described the level of practical or technical expertise, whilst present, need not be the primary qualification. Other systems, if they place a greater responsibility for the work produced upon the Quality Manager, create a greater need for technical knowledge. However both BS 7229 and BS 5750 indicate the need to separate the management of the system from the management of the physical work to ensure that those responsible for the work remain responsible. Finally it must also be recognised that there is a need for training such an individual. This should be directed not only to their audit function but also to ensure management's general responsibility under Clause 4.1. This Clause requires management to ensure each person's ability to undertake whatever role is assigned to them.

9.2.3 Where

So where do you place this person in the management structure? Clearly this is a management role and as such should have a well defined and clear status within the company's structure. This will probably be at departmental manager level or equivalent. In part this conclusion is drawn from the observation that the higher the status of the individual the less that person is likely to require, or indeed use, their authority. The Quality Management function need not be the sole function of the individual appointed, although this will vary dependent upon the size of the organisation. If this function is only part of the person's duties then it is important that the other function/s is perceived as commensurate with the status noted previously.

9.2.4 When

The next question is when should you appoint or nominate a person to this role? As was shown in our discussion of the early stages of the implementation of the system there is a role for a Quality Manager as early as the investigation stage. There is a need within any organisation contemplating the development of a QA system, demonstrated in Fig 1.3 (page 9), for an individual at management level who can combine a level of understanding of QA with the knowledge of the functioning of the organisation. Our discussion on familiarisation later in this chapter reinforces this need.

9.2.5 What

A typical job description for a QA Manager might therefore list the following duties:
- guidance and support in preparation of the QA system
- appraisal and approval to changes in procedures
- regular review of quality documentation
- preparation of audit programmes
- responsibility for conducting internal audits
- responsibility for conducting external audits of subcontractors and suppliers
- guidance in preparation of project Quality Plans
- reviewing recruitment and training procedures implementation.

9.3   Recruitment, Education and Training

Recruitment, education and training must be viewed as the management of an important intangible asset. Companies recognise that in order to manage assets, information is required as to their value and condition and much effort is devoted to this end. Clause 4.1 requires management to ascertain both these things, furthermore under Clause 4.17 they are required to record in writing, that they have done so, and to retain such records for inspection. Also, where a deficiency in respect of the individual's experience, qualifications or training, with regard to their present or proposed role, is identified, they are required to rectify the deficiency. Clause 4.17 advises that particular attention should be given to new staff, thus recruitment, education and training become closely linked. Procedures written for this section of the Manual for training should also address recruitment where stricter selection of new staff linked to a long term strategy and career structures could assist in improving the skills base of the company. A particular problem relates to existing staff who may lack formal training or qualifications but this should be catered for by formally excluding staff with 'x' years experience in a particular role from these procedures.

The procedures would then address seven areas:

1. Selection methods, interview techniques.
2. Records of checks on references/qualification.
3. Staff records, qualifications and experience.
4. Training records.
5. Education programmes.
6. Career structure plan.
7. Management responsibility via a delegated structure.

The final point notes the need for the individual's own manager to be given responsibility for monitoring that person's career plan. The managers would then, in turn, be monitored by their immediate superiors.

9.4 Familiarisation

As you will have noted we have suggested that this process is something that must take place from the initial stages of the systems development. The reason for early familiarisation is to foster a sense of involvement in a process of change which will inevitably create some anxiety and even resistance. In addition an early introduction to the principles of the system to be produced is essential to allow the two way flow of information necessary for its development. This is also clearly not the only point at which familiarisation is necessary.

Every effort should be made to produce a system which is clear and easy to use. In attempting to do this there is a problem that you immediately encounter. The sheer volume of paperwork necessary to write something which needs no further explanation often defeats the other objective, that of ease of use. A compromise is to accept that the processes of use and familiarisation with the system could be separated. This can be done by devising introductory seminars or training for groups of staff preferably in cross disciplinary teams. This can be done by a regular programme of seminars initially to cover all personnel but later to specifically targeted groups of staff or areas of operation. An example of this was previously referred to in Chapter 8 under 8.2 Quality Plan procedures as a course of instruction in the preparation of Quality Plans. Seminars also provide an opportunity to exchange views on current procedures.

In addition to the seminars it is necessary to set up a programme of continuing debate on quality or quality system problems which could well be linked to a formal feedback process.

This page intentionally left blank

10.0   Introduction

This chapter illustrates edited copies of all forms referred to in the Flow Charts or General Procedures described in the preceding Chapters.

As stated the forms are mainly checklists serving to add flesh to the tasks outlined in the flow charts or described in the procedures. Alternatively they provide a list of the points required to be raised within the agendas of meetings that occur at particular stages. The forms when completed will be stored in the Records Section of the filing system described within the Document Control procedures see Chapter 8.

Our research has shown that the simple act of completing and storing a form known to contain particular information can save considerable time and paperwork. An example of this can be illustrated by reference to the first form, QA/A the Enquiry Report, on the next page. The form sets out the basic tendering information of project particulars, contract details, methods of tendering and staff involved. This information is required at frequent intervals during each of the stages e.g. tender preparation, handing over stage, introduction of subcontractors, completion of subsidiary documentation etc. Checking past project records revealed that the information shown had been abstracted from source and written down on numerous occasions, sometimes by the same individual. This fact is true of many other sets or pieces of information.

Although completion of the forms appears at first sight to be an addition to the paper mountain already generated, this is not so. The forms, rather than being a generator of paperwork, are a known data source which saves abortive time and paperwork spent on tasks which are often needlessly repeated.

Examination of the forms will reveal that they do not involve additional tasks, merely the recording of those tasks which should be completed in the course of the individual satisfactorily executing normal duties.

PROJECT PARTICULARS

Project description	Project address
Date enquiry received	Date tender to be submitted
Project type	Client
	Contact
	Telephone
Architect	Engineer
Contact	Contact
Telephone	Telephone
Quantity Surveyor	Drawings available at
Contact	By arrangement with
Telephone	

CONTRACT DETAILS

Form of Contract			Method of measurement		
Amendments			Insurances		
Special Conditions					
Fixed price	Period		Bond		
Fluctuating-type	Clause no.		Base month		Non-adjustable%
Period certificates	Monthly/other		Period for payment..... days		
Retention	Certified value%		Materials	%	Limit of Retention
Liquidated damages	£....................week/day		Defects liability period		.................months.
Commence date	Complete date		Sectional completion		

METHOD OF TENDERING

Traditional	Form of tender	Design & Build	Feasibility Report
	Bills of quantities		Form of tender
	Schedule of rates		Drawings
			Bills of Quantities
			Schedule of rates
Category A B C D		Type	Feasibility
Initial Category			Budget
Revised Category			Final tender
Drawings to prepare Yes/No		Bills to prepare	Yes/No

ESTIMATORS REPORT

Adequacy of information			
Contract period	Own assessment	Any phasing	Mobilisation

STAFF ALLOCATED

Estimator -name/s	Project co-ord-name/s
Planner-name/s	Site staff-name/s
Others-specify	

QA MANUAL	Programme and Method Review Report	SECTION	Supporting Documentation		
		STAGE	Tender		
		REF	QAM 5.1	QA/B1	
		REV		DATE	
		SHEET	1	of	1

PARTICULARS

Project name	Brief description

TIMESCALE

		Comments
Programme time	Specified	
	Anticipated	
Phasing	Client requirements	
	Contractor requirements	
Major gang sizes		
Major plant outputs		

CONSTRUCTION

List of major work packages	Subcontracts	Response	Onerous conditions	Particular attendance

Material / Plant problems	Delivery	Advance orders	Special storage	Other

Labour / staff problems	Availability	Transportation	Other

Logistic problems	Access	Services	Tips	Other

PARTICULARS

Project name	Brief description

ANALYSIS

High rates / Low rates	BQ ref	Own Rates			S/c Rates	Comment	Amended	
		Lab	Plant	Mats			Yes	No

Attendance / Prelims		Comment	Response	Amended	
High / low	BQ ref			Yes	No

Project name		Ref	Date

NOTES

The choice of company whilst generally being of the enquirer's own preference should also conform with one of the following criteria.

A. A specified company subject to Note 1 below

B. Companies included within the approved list

C. Other companies subject to checking procedure by Estimator (checking procedures QA/F)

Note 1 - companies should be checked by Estimator. If they fail to conform the client should be notified.

MATERIALS				SUBCONTRACTORS			
SUPPLIER	Cat	✔	Date	SUBCONTRACTOR	Cat	✔	Date

QA MANUAL	Enquiry Records (contd)	SECTION	Supporting Documentation	
		STAGE	Tender/Mobilisation/Construction	
		REF	QAM 5.1	QA/C (contd)
		REV	DATE	
		SHEET	of	

MATERIALS				SUBCONTRACTORS			
SUPPLIER	Cat	✔	Date	SUBCONTRACTOR	Cat	✔	Date

QUALITY ASSURANCE

QA MANUAL	Site Visit Report	SECTION	Supporting Documentation		
		STAGE	Tender		
		REF	QAM 5.1	QA/D	
		REV		DATE	
		SHEET	1	of	3

Project name		Ref	
HEADINGS		**REMARKS**	

HEADINGS		REMARKS
CONTRACT DETAILS		
Site Address		
General Description		
EXISTING SITE DETAILS		
Buildings		
Services	Telephone	
	Gas	
	Water	
	Electric	
Obstructions & Restraints		
Fences or Hoardings		
Trees,streams etc.		
Access		
Location in relation to:	Road	
	Rail	
	Public transport	
Conditions of traffic on		
highways adjacent to site		
Parking restrictions / nearest available		
SERVICES (Nearest available)		
	Telephone	
	Gas	
	Water	
	Electric	
Drains		
	Foul	
	Surface water	

HEADINGS		REMARKS
GROUND CONDITIONS		
Topography		
	Flat	
	Sloping/Flat	
	Sloping	
Borehole details		
	Location	
	Type of surface soil	
	Stability	
	Visible water table	
Soil storage		
	Location	
	Drainage	
	Disposal	
OTHER SERVICES		
General	Local authority	
	Police	
	Hospital	
Suppliers		
	Builders merchants	
	Ready-mix concrete	
	Quarries	
	Others specified	
Tips		
	Distance	
	Charges	
	Exclusions	
TEMPORARY WORKS		
Offices/storage	Position	
	Services	
	Movement	
Access roads/hard standing		
	Existing	
	New	
Signs		
	Directional	
	Advertising	
Existing buildings		
	Protection	
	Demolition	

HEADINGS	REMARKS
GENERAL DETAILS	
Mileage to Office	
Projects in area	
Local s/contractors	
Local plant supply	
General weather	
Exposure index	
Rainfall pattern	
Temperatures	
Type of adjacent buildings	
Residential	
Industrial	
Commercial	
Others (specify)	
NAMES/VISITING PARTIES	
Estimator	
Site staff	
Planner	
Contracts manager	
Project co-ordinator	
Others (specify)	
SKETCHES/PHOTOS	
List	
ANY OTHER DETAILS	
PREPARED BY	
Name	Position
Signature	Date

AGENDA

Project name	Ref
Date of initial review meeting	Tender date
Present	

ESTABLISHMENT OF TIMETABLE

Latest date for	Date	Action	Latest date for	Date	Action
Despatch of enquiries			Finalise programme		
Receipt of quotations			Contract Review Meeting		
Visit to site			Category Review Meeting		
Finalise method statement			Prog. & Method Review Meeting		
Complete cost estimate			Tender Review Meeting		

QUALITY OF TENDER INFORMATION

Drawings	Comment	Action	Bills of Quantities	Comment	Action
Location			Preliminaries		
Layout			Preambles		
Construction:- Architectural			Measured work		
Structural			Sketches		
M&E			**Specification**		
Others					

TENDER INCEPTION DISCUSSION

Schedule of trades to be sub-contracted

Major materials and plant items

Site set up / staffing

ADDITIONAL ITEMS

CHECKING PROCEDURES - NEW FIRMS :- Firms under Category C
(or A where applicable)

Project name	Ref
Company name	Address
Checked by	Date

Note: If successful the company's name must be added to the Central Data Bank and a copy of this form filed in their records as well as the Tender / Contract Records File.

SUPPLIER	SUBCONTRACTOR
Points to establish	
(1) Do the Company's products comply with a recognised / specified standard i.e.	(1) Does the Company's work comply with a recognised / specified / approved standard i.e.
Tick	
a. has a BS Kitemark	Tick
b. has a BBA Certificate	a. a registered QA System BS 5750
c. has a Test Certificate from other body	b. other QA System - 1st or 2nd Party certified
d. will provide own written warranty	c. suitable confirmed 3rd Party references
e. inspection and written assurance	d. successful inspection of previous work
f. other - specify	e. other - specify
(2) Do they manufacture to a consistent quality	*Note if the S/c is also supplying materials he will be required to check and verify conformance of*
Tick	*his materials in accordance with the criteria*
a. a registered QA System BS 5750	*listed in the Materials column as a condition of*
b. other QA System - 1st or 2nd Party	*their order*
c. inspection visits of previous projects	
d. other - specify	

Reason for conformance should be entered in the 'checked' column of QA / C

Example	
Supplier	**Subcontractor**
Conformance may therefore be entered in the column as:	Conformance may therefore be entered in the column as:
1(a) / 2(b)	1(a)

NOTE - it is important that copies of documents establishing conformance above must be obtained by theArea Office Contracts Dept. whilst placing the order.

QA MANUAL	Contract Review	SECTION	Supporting Documentation	
		STAGE	Tender	
		REF	QAM 5.1	QA/G
		REV	DATE	
		SHEET	1	of	1

AGENDA

Project name	Ref
1. Details of client or holding company	
2. Full particulars of consultants to be used including duties and responsibilities	
3. Particulars of site supervision to be provided by client/consultants	
4. Has tender been subject to a previous invitation	
5. Number of tenders to be invited	
6. Date for commmencement (actual)	
7. Details of any phasing	
8. An outline of method of construction	
9. Access problems	
10. Details of Nominated S/c or Suppliers	
11. Amendments to Standard Form of Contract	
12. Bonding requirements	
13. Insurance requirements	
14. Stage of Design (i) today (ii) at commencement	
15. Any particular requirements / problems	
16. Unclear Specification items	
17. Unclear Drawing details	
18. Unclear Bill of Quantities items	

QA MANUAL	Tender Review Record	SECTION	Supporting Documentation	
		STAGE	Tender	
		REF	QAM 5.1	QA/H
		REV	DATE	
		SHEET	1 of	1

PARTICULARS

Project name	Description
Date received	Date due Time
Tender to be delivered to	

ATTENDANCE

INFORMATION

Enquiry Report	
Form B1	
Form B2	

DISCUSSION

Form B1	
Form B2	
Overheads and profit	

DECISIONS

Record of decisions taken	Action by

QA MANUAL	Appointment Procedures	SECTION	Supporting Documentation		
		STAGE	Tender/Mobilisation/Construction		
		REF	QAM 5.1	QA/K	
		REV		DATE	
		SHEET	1	of	1

Project name	Ref

GENERAL NOTE

If Consultants are to be chosen via these procedures the information necessary for Section B will be derived either

(1) from records of a previous interview and telephone conversation or

(2) interview specifically for this project

SECTION A

Scope of work	Company A	Company B	Company C

SECTION B

Experience of project type			
Experienced with Client			
Requirements			
a. timetable			
b. fee			
c. quality *			
d. insurance			
e. contract			

SECTION C

Details of agreement			

NOTES

* Quality requirements either (1) QA System to BS 5750 or (2) own QA System or (3) inspection visit

QA MANUAL	Handover Meeting Record	SECTION	Supporting Documentation	
		STAGE	Mobilisation	
		REF	QAM 5.1	QA/L
		REV		DATE
		SHEET	1	of	1

PARTICULARS

Project name	Site Address
Meeting Date	Site Telephone No.

ATTENDANCE

Information handed over	No. copies	Action		No. copies	Action
Enquiry Report			Bills of Quantities		
✓ Site Visit Report			Tender Drawings and Spec		
Form B1			Net & Gross Printouts		
Form B2			Prelims Build-up		
✓ Tender Review Record			Rates Build-up		
Enquiry Record			✓ S/c and Supplier Quotes		
			Resourced Tender Prog.		

POINTS OF DISCUSSION	Notes
Contract Conditions	
The Site	
Method and Programme	
Tender Build-up	
Client / Information Appraisal	
Other	

Project name		Ref	
Date of Meeting		Site Commencement Date	

ATTENDANCE

MOBILISATION TIMETABLE

Item	Latest date	Action by	Item	Latest date	Action by
Check / arrange services			Finalise main programme		
Arrange site photos / survey			Prepare detail sub- progs.		
Open local accounts			Prepare initial histograms		
Arrange site offices, store etc.			Analyse temp. works required		
Review method of work			Prepare quality plan		
Prepare cost monitoring info.			Pre-commence Client meeting		
Establish safety policy			Pre-commence Co-ord meeting		
Set up doc. control					

QUALITY OF CONSTRUCTION INFORMATION

Item	Comment	Date for receipt	Action by
Drawings			
Location			
Layout & Elevation			
Construction			
Architectural			
Structural			
M&E			
Others			

QUALITY ASSURANCE

SUPPLIERS / SUBCONTRACTORS

Schedule of trades to be subcontracted (Initial Review)

Trade	Action by	Trade	Action by	Trade	Action by

Schedule of materials and plant to be ordered (Initial Review)

Item	Action by	Item	Action by	Item	Action by

Site set up / staffing

Item	Action by	Item	Action by	Item	Action by

Other

QA MANUAL	Contract Review (Stage 2)	SECTION		Supporting Documentation	
		STAGE		Mobilisation	
		REF	QAM 5.1	QA/N	
		REV		DATE	
		SHEET	1	of	1

AGENDA FOR CONTRACT REVIEW MEETING WITH CLIENT
(STAGE 2 PRE-COMMENCEMENT) * Refer to QA/G

Project name	Ref
Date of meeting	Venue

ATTENDANCE

Contractor	Client	Position	Tel No.

INFORMATION FROM CLIENT	INFORMATION FROM CONTRACTOR
Date for possession	Project team
Schedule of tests / samples	Construction programme
Bond	Quality plan (initial period)
Insurances	Office accommodation
Particular client procedures	Date for commencement)
Nominations	Particular Company procedures
Provisional sums	
Contract signature / completion	

DRAWINGS / SPECIFICATION AVAILABLE / IN PREPARATION

Item	Ref No.	Rec. date	Anticipated date

FURTHER INFORMATION

Unclear Specification items	
Unclear Drawing details	
Unclear BQ details	
Date of next meeting	Venue

Project name		Ref	
Date of Meeting		Venue	

ATTENDANCE

PROGRESS REVIEW MOBILISATION TIMETABLE

Item	Complete	Action by	Item	Complete	Action by
Check / arrange services	✓		Finalise main programme		
Arrange site photos / survey	✓		Prep. detailed sub-progs.		
Open local accounts			Prepare initial histograms		
Arrange site offices, store etc.			Analyse temp. works required		
Review method of work	✓		Prepare quality plan		
Prepare cost monitoring inf.	✓				
Establish safety policy	✓				
Set up doc. control	✓				

QUALITY OF CONSTRUCTION INFORMATION (UPDATE AND REVIEW)

Drawings received	Comments	Action by

Drawings awaited	Due by date	Action by

RESULTS OF EXAMINATION OF DRAWINGS / SPECIFICATION

Items requiring Architect's approval / action

Item	Ref	Item	Ref	Item	Ref

Items which are unusual / problems

Item	Ref	Item	Ref	Item	Ref

SUPPLIERS / SUBCONTRACTORS

Trades / item - ordered	Trades / item - enquiries sent	No. sent	No. retnd	Action by

SITE / PROJECT MANAGEMENT

Discuss / complete staff organisation chart	Action by

Staff job descriptions issued (*see Standard Descriptions QA Manual **)*

Name	Position	Name	Position	Name	Position

QA MANUAL	Site (co-ordination) Meeting Timetable	SECTION	Supporting Documentation		
		STAGE	Construction		
		REF	QAM 5.1	QA/Q	
		REV		DATE	
		SHEET	1	of	1

Project name	Ref

Name of subcontractor / consultant

Address	Telephone No.

Representative to contact	Extension No.

Venue for meetings	
Time of meetings	

Contractor's representative to contact	Telephone No.

Directions to venue

TIMETABLE

Date for possession	S/c commencement date
Date for completion	S/c completion date
E.O.T. granted to main contractor	E.O.T. granted to S/c
Details of phasing	Details of phasing

Meeting No.	Date	S/c required to attend	Meeting No.	Date	S/c required to attend
1			22		
2			23		
3			24		
4			25		
5			26		
6			27		
7			28		
8			29		
9			30		
10			31		
11			32		
12			33		
13			34		
14			35		
15			36		
16			37		
17			38		
18			39		
19			40		
20			41		
21			42		

Note: Please confirm your ability to attend

* Revisions to the timetable to be issued if necessary on this form

QA MANUAL	Site Construction Co-ordination Meeting	SECTION	Supporting Documentation	
		STAGE	Construction	
		REF	QAM 5.1	QA/R
		REV		DATE
		SHEET	1	of

AGENDA

Project name   Ref

Meeting No.   Venue   Date

Present

Agree minutes of previous meeting	Yes	No

Errors or omissions

Record of inclement weather in period   to date

Detailed progress report related to programme and agreed with client's representative (see Sheet 3)

Check action required from previous minutes

List items dealt with	Action

List items outstanding One month	

Longer

Instructions issued in the period

Drawings / Information issued in the period

C.O.W. Directions issued in the period

REQUESTS FOR INFORMATION IN PERIOD

Ref No.	Date sent	Date replied	Date part replied	Info. outstanding	No reply

QA MANUAL	Site Construction Co-ordination Meeting (contd)	SECTION		Supporting Documentation	
		STAGE		Construction	
		REF	QAM 5.1	QA/R	
		REV		DATE	
		SHEET		of	

REQUESTS FOR INSPECTION IN PERIOD

Ref No.	Date	Result	Date	Action

DELAY NOTIFICATIONS TO DATE

Contractor

Ref No.	Date	Reply received	Action required

Subcontractor

Ref No.	Date	Reply received	Action required

Any other business	Action

Date for next meeting if not as scheduled	Venue if not as scheduled

Progress listing % complete against programme operations

Operation	Programme %	Actual %

AGENDA

Project name   Ref

Meeting No.	Venue		Date

Present

Agree minutes of previous meeting	Yes	No

Errors or omissions

Record of inclement weather in period   to date

Subcontractors' progress reports related to programme and agreed with contractor's representative (see Sheet 3)

Check action required from previous minutes

List items dealt with	Action

List items outstanding One month	

Longer	

Subcontract instructions issued in period to each S/c (S/c listed in alphabetical order)-enter latest reference number

Name	Ref no.	Name	Ref no.

Drawings issued in period (S/c listed in alphabetical order)

QA MANUAL	Site Subcontractors Co-ordination Meeting (contd)	SECTION		Supporting Documentation	
		STAGE		Construction	
		REF	QAM 5.1	QA/R(s)	
		REV		DATE	
		SHEET		of	

S/c Quality Plans

Name	Up to date?	Action

Test / Inspection certificates supplied in period (S/c listed in alphabetical order)

Name	No.	Name	No.

Work stoppage certificates issued - this period

Work stoppage certificates issued - previous period

Work stoppage certificates released

Any other business	Action

Date for next meeting if not as scheduled	Venue if not as scheduled

QA MANUAL	Site Subcontractors Co-ordination Meeting (contd)	SECTION	Supporting Documentation	
		STAGE	Construction	
		REF	QAM 5.1	QA/R(s)
		REV		
		SHEET	DATE of	

Progress listing % complete against programme operations

Operation	Programme %	Actual %

Project name		Month	Year
Ref		Date prepared	

PROGRESS

Programme Ref		Revision		Date	

Progress listing % complete against programme operations

Operation No.	Programme %	Actual %	Operation No.	Programme %	Actual %

Note numbers here of operations which were completed during previous period

Contract completion date		EOT claimed	*Days
Revised completion date		EOT granted	*Days
Estimated completion date		EOT not claimed	*Days
* Working days		EOT rejected	*Days

RESOURCES

Labour	Approx hours/value re-sourced	Approx hours/value ex-pended
Own labour		
S/c labour		
Own staff		
Agency staff		

RESOURCES (CONTD)

Major plant	Approx hours resourced to date	Approx hours expended to date

Mark own (o) or hired (h)

Major subcontractors	Programme		Comments	No. QA/W certs issued in period
	OK	(+) / (-)		

RESOURCES (CONTD)

Major materials in period	Quantity in valuation	Quantity delivered	Quantity in stock	% waste

INFORMATION

	No. issued		Answered		Unanswered	
	To date	Period	To date	Period	To date	Period
Information requests (QA/U)						
Information appraisal (QA/V)						
Inspection requests (QA/W)						

	No. issued	
	To date	Period
Confirmation of verbal instructions (QA/X)		
Architects / SO instructions		
C.O.W directions		
Subcontractor / supplier instructions		

Drawings

	Latest Ref No.	No. in period
Architects / SO		
Subcontractors		
Suppliers		
M & E		
Others		

INFORMATION (CONTD)

	Latest Ref No.	No. in period
Letters from Architect		
Letters to Architect		
Letters from S/c / Suppliers		
Letters to S/C /Suppliers		
Others (list)		

Resource problems - (note particular problems including information)

Enclose copies of the following

    Final account progress report

    Loss damage or injury report

    Diary pages for period

    Test / inspection certificates

    Minutes of latest site co-ordination meetings

    Estimator feedback FormQA/Z

    Others (list)

SITE MANAGER'S COMMENTS

Signed   Date

QA MANUAL	Information Request	SECTION	Supporting Documentation	
		STAGE	Construction	
		REF	QAM 5.1	QA/U
		REV		DATE
		SHEET	1	of	1

Project name   Ref

Date

Description

Date required by   Signed

Reply

Date   Signed

QA MANUAL	Information receipt/ appraisal	SECTION	Supporting Documentation		
		STAGE	Construction		
		REF	QAM 5.1	QA/V	
		REV		DATE	
		SHEET	1	of	1

Project name	Ref
Document received	
Document ref. (from DC /1)	
Date	
Checked by	

OK to proceed	Query or extra information

Information required

Date required by

Signed   Date

QA MANUAL	Work Inspection Certificate	SECTION		Supporting Documentation	
		STAGE		Construction	
		REF	QAM 5.1		QA/W
		REV		DATE	
		SHEET		of	

Subcontractor or own work

Project name			Ref			
Date						
Subcontractor name			Person responsible			
Operation number		Description				

Hold points	Description	Checked by	Proceed date	Hold date	Released date

Waivers

Hold points	Description of waiver	Date

QA MANUAL	Receipt of Confirmation of Verbal Instructions	SECTION	Supporting Documentation		
		STAGE	Construction		
		REF	QAM 5.1	QA/X	
		REV		DATE	
		SHEET	1	of	1

Project name   Ref

Date

Verbal instruction from   Date

Description of Instruction

Forward to Architect within seven days of verbal instructions

NOTE - Reference any follow up correspondence from Architect here

QA MANUAL	Material/Plant Confirmation Receipt	SECTION	Supporting Documentation	
		STAGE	Construction	
		REF	QAM 5.1	QA/Y
		REV	DATE	
		SHEET	of	

Project name				Ref
Date				

Brief Description	Delivery Note Number	Date	Inspected by *	Comments

* Authorised persons nominated by the site manager only

QA MANUAL	Estimator Feedback	SECTION		Supporting Documentation		
		STAGE		Construction		
		REF	QAM 5.1		QA/Z	
		REV		DATE		
		SHEET	1	of		3

Project name		Ref	
Report No.	Issued by	Date	

Subcontractor	Performance Rating	Comments

Performance Rating - * Very Poor ** Poor *** Satisfactory **** Good

Supplier	Performance Rating	Comments

Consultants	Performance rating	Comments

Performance Rating - * Very Poor ** Poor *** Satisfactory **** Good

Rate build-up variances

BQ Item	Rate (nett)	Cost	Any special circumstances	Other Comments

This page intentionally left blank

11.0　Generally

Having described the process of implementing a QA system and examined its constituent parts you will have observed that it is a complex and lengthy process. This is not the end of the development of the system.

It is after all the time and effort expended in producing the initial system that a dangerous point is reached. The danger is that once the system is **complete** it will become a neatly packaged inviolate document. This is the very thing that must be avoided and positive action must be taken to prevent it. It is management's role within the system to ensure its maintenance and a sure sign for an auditor that a system is not working is the absence of change.

QA is about getting it right first time but this is an aim that will forever remain on the horizon; the important thing is that the journey is in the right direction. Having prepared the manual a culture must be developed by the company within the individuals who use the system to question and improve the procedures used. Both management and individuals must aim for improvement and appreciate that evolutionary change is essential to take the path that leads in the direction of getting it right first time.

For the purposes of obtaining British Standards certification it is wise not to include more than is necessary within the audited procedures. From the alternative viewpoint of improving the organisation's efficiency it makes sense that all areas of the company should eventually be encompassed within a broader system. The discipline inherent in a QA system can improve the way all activities are undertaken. The requirements of the British Standard draw in those activities that have a primary relationship with the finished product. Activities such as marketing and accountancy may have only a secondary relationship but their efficiency is important to the organisation as a whole.

To conclude therefore it may be helpful to abstract the key points brought out in the previous chapters.

11.1　Summary of 20 key points

Point 1
QA is not an optional extra but a philosophy that management must be committed to.

◆ Chapter 1

Point 2

A QA system to have any credibility must comply with BS 5750 or its European or International equivalent.

◆ Chapters 1 and 3

Point 3

The production of a QA system encounters two major problems:

- the volume of work it requires
- blending a knowledge of QA and the organisation.

◆ Chapter 1

Point 4

Involve employees early in order to:

- avoid creating unnecessary concern or antipathy
- instigate a sense of property.

◆ Chapter 3

Point 5

Use graphics as an aid to conveying information.

◆ Chapter 3

Point 6

Note the aspects of a good system illustrated by Rudyard Kipling's six servants.

◆ Chapters 3 and 4

Point 7

The QA manual should be established as the company's main reference document.

◆ Chapter 3

Point 8

Construction based QA systems operate at two levels:

- company wide
- project specific.

◆ Chapters 2, 4 &and 8

Point 9

The QA manual describes the way an organisation conducts its business.

◆ Chapter 2

Point 10
The manual must be available to all with roles or responsibilities within it.

◆ Chapter 2

Point 11
Distribution of the manual and amendments must be controlled and recorded.

◆ Chapters 2 and 4

Point 12
Company organisation charts are best developed in two tiers:

- central administrative organisation
- project based organisation.

◆ Chapter 4

Point 13
The manual is simplified if developed relative to the different groups involved:

- tender
- mobilisation
- construction stages.

◆ Chapter 4

Point 14
Describing what is done is extremely complex so layer the information e.g. flow charts, procedures and forms.

◆ Chapters 4-7

Point 15
Meetings should be kept brief but are a useful aid to communication.

◆ Chapter 4

Point 16
Time, resources, information and control pose problems at all stages which must be addressed and controlled.

◆ Chapters 4-7

Point 17

The quality plan is completed pre-construction but tiering again helps giving:

- overall plan
- necessary detail.

◆ Chapter 8

Point 18

Internal audits check the system not the work, responsibility remains with management at all levels.

◆ Chapter 9

Point 19

Employees are an important bought-in resource controlled via recruitment and training.

◆ Chapter 9

Point 20

Communication equates with good management and should be incorporated wherever possible within the QA system.

◆ Chapter 3

Finally remember your QA system is a live thing that must encourage a two-way flow of information as it must change to improve. To quote from Sir Winston Churchill:

There is nothing wrong with change if it is in the right direction. To improve is to change, so to be perfect is to have changed often.

A

Audit
clause 4.16   23
construction stage   85
internal   23, 36
manual   41
mobilisation stage   79
process   121-2
tender stage   51

B

British Standards
4778 : Part 1 : 1987   6, 15
5750 : Part 1 : 1987   8, 11
5750 : Part 2 : 1987   8, 11-12, 42, 49
5750 : Part 3 : 1987   11
5750 : Part 4 : 1990   11-12, 41, 121
5750 diagram   13
5750 philosophy   11
7229 : 1989   121

C

Certification
accredited bodies   27, 38
first party   25, 27
second party   25, 27
third party   27
Client
assurance   11
requirements   16
supplied services   18
Contract Review
clause 4.3   16
construction stage   84
mobilisation stage   78

tender stage   50
Corrective Action
clause 4.13   20

D

Defects   4
Document Control
clause 4.4   17
construction stage   84
drawing register   17, 97, 102
mobilisation stage   79
procedures   97, 99-103
system   17
tender stage   51
Documentary Evidence   1, 15

E

Equipment Test
clause 4.10   20

F

Flow Charts
report   33
system   44-5
Form of Contract
implications   3, 51
Forms
examples   128-65
manual   41-42
purpose   44

G

Government Grant   27

H

Handling and Storage
    clause 4.14   21
    construction stage   85

I

Implementation   8, 25
Inspection and Testing
    clause 4.9   20
    construction stage   85
Inspection/Test Status
    clause 4.11   20

K

Knowledge Continuum   9

M

Management
    clause 4.1   14, 17
    construction stage   84
    factors   1, 43
    mobilisation stage   78
    problems   42, 49-50, 77, 83
    tender stage   50
Method Statements   19

N

Non-conformance Control
    clause 4.12   20

O

Organisation
    analysis   28
    BS requirements   34
    company manuals   32
    documentary evidence   30
    interviews   29
    questionnaires   29
    report   30, 33
    roles and responsibilities   31
    site personnel   32
    structure   30
    support departments   31

P

Process Control
    clause 4.8   19
    construction stage   85
    mobilisation stage   79
    tender stage   51
Purchasing
    clause 4.5   18
    construction stage   84
    mobilisation stage   79
    tender stage   51

Q

QA
    consultants   10, 27
    manager   10, 123-24
    optional extra   9
    problems   9
    system   6, 8
QA System
    clause 4.2   15
    construction stage   84
    how   35, 44
    mobilisation   77
    mobilisation stage   78
    operation   47
    philosophy   42
    structure   39
    tender stage   50
    what   35, 44
    when   35, 44
    where   35, 44
    who   35, 44
    why   35, 44
Quality
    definition   6
    manual   15

plan	16
records	17, 51, 79, 85
records clause 4.15	22

Quality Assurance

advantages	7
cost	7
disadvantages	7
how	5
management system	2, 5
what	6
why	3

Quality Manual

construction stage	41, 86-95
control system	39, 41
director's statement	39, 41
document control	41
general procedures	41, 44
mobilisation stage	41, 80-81
organisation chart	40-41
staged procedures	41
supporting documentation	41-42
tender stage	41, 43, 54-75

Quality Plan

BS requirements	15
contents	114-17
detailed	85, 109-10, 116
general	104, 108, 115
manual	41
procedures	97, 104-17
subcontractors	112-13, 117
test/inspection	111

S

Specified Requirements	12, 18, 79

Stages

development	25, 35
instigation	25, 27
investigation	25, 27
testing	25, 35

Statistical Techniques

clause 4.18	20
construction stage	85
Supervision	5

T

Timescale	27

Traceability

clause 4.7	18

Training

clause 4.17	24
construction stage	85
familiarisation	125
manual	41
mobilisation stage	79
new personnel	24
personnel records	24, 124-25
quality awareness	24, 28, 36
tender stage	52

W

Works Guidance Notes

example	118-19
manual	41-42